WOODLAND MANAGEMENT
FOR PHEASANTS & WILDLIFE

WOODLAND MANAGEMENT
FOR PHEASANTS & WILDLIFE

NIGEL GRAY

DAVID & CHARLES
Newton Abbot London North Pomfret (Vt)

All photographs (unless otherwise stated)
are by the author and members of the staff
of The Game Conservancy

British Library Cataloguing in Publication Data

Gray, Nigel
  Woodland management for pheasants and wildlife.
  1. Forest conservation – Great Britain
  2. Forest management – Great Britain
  I. Title
  333.75′0941   SD414.G7

  ISBN 0-7153-8883-5

Typeset by Typesetters (Birmingham) Ltd
Smethwick West Midlands
and printed in Great Britain
by Redwood Burn Limited Trowbridge Wilts
for David & Charles Publishers plc
Brunel House Newton Abbot Devon

Published in the United States of America
by David & Charles Inc
North Pomfret Vermont 05053 USA

Contents

Throughout this book the emphasis is on good sporting pheasants (*Gordon Carlisle*)

Foreword

Back in 1955 with burgeoning thoughts about the improvement of the Stratfield Saye shoot, I sought the help of the old Eley Game Advisory Service. As a result, a young ex-naval officer named Nigel Gray arrived, full of ideas and enthusiasm. Over the years I have been fortunate enough to count him as a friend and have the benefit of his advice. That advice has been immensely valuable. Nigel's extensive knowledge ranges from pure forestry and agriculture, through a far-reaching understanding of the pheasant and its habits, to a deep insight and love of the countryside and its conservation. All his immense fund of knowledge is contained in this book.

I do not want to insult him by saying that he thinks like a pheasant – we all know that the average reared pheasant is a pretty idiotic creature, at least in early life. Let me rather equate his understanding of pheasant behaviour to the habits of the wily January cock who will outwit the best of us!

I can thoroughly recommend this book to all who love the country-side and the pleasure it gives us when we go shooting. For me the knowledge it contains has given me two precious gifts. The first is a better understanding of the nature of game habitat, which is, of course, of benefit to all wildlife, and my efforts to improve that habitat have given me enormous satisfaction. The second is the pleasure I have had over the years in managing my shoot to produce the most testing birds possible in a countryside which is not naturally endowed with valleys and hills. I hope Nigel Gray's fund of expertise will do the same for all who read his book.

His Grace The Duke of Wellington, MVO, OBE, MC

7

The author's family wishes to thank Charles Coles
(former Director of The Game Conservancy)
for helping in the production of this book
following the death of Nigel Gray

Preface

From 1950 to 1980 I worked at the Game Research Station at Fording-bridge, Hampshire, owned successively by Imperial Chemical Industries, Imperial Metal Industries and now by the Game Conservancy. During these years, I spent most of my time advising tenants and owners of shoots how to improve their sport. This work was mainly in the south-east of England, although there have been many forays into all parts of Britain and Ireland as well as Holland, Denmark, Germany, France, Belgium and, on one outstanding occasion, Iran! During the course of this work I have surveyed nearly 1,500 shoots covering approximately 2½ million acres (and incidentally motored nearly a million miles). I can therefore claim a fairly broad experience of game management.

More than half of my work has concerned habitat improvement, less in the 1950s but to an increasing extent as the damaging effects of modern forestry and agriculture began to be felt in the 1960s, and a new horror became apparent – the 'conifer syndrome'. The prevailing entrenched view that saw game and forestry as competing alternatives added to the problem. Few gamekeepers had more than a nodding acquaintance with the techniques of forestry; they regarded the woodlands as game sanctuaries which must be kept undisturbed at all cost and resented the intrusion of the forester. Similarly, the forester rarely had any knowledge of game management (though a few enjoyed shooting) and mostly regarded the gamekeeper as a nuisance.

In this situation it was obviously necessary for the game manager to look at the problems quite dispassionately to see if a compromise could be found. This is what I did, and was agreeably surprised to find that it was perfectly possible to include the requirements of game in the commercial forestry plan with no inconvenience (in fact usually the reverse), and very little direct cost or loss of income.

In the late 1950s I wrote the first of the ICI Game Service's booklets on the subject, a booklet that was freely distributed. But, alas, a mere booklet does not change attitudes, particularly those bred from animosity. And so the destruction of many acres of our game coverts continued apace until the disfiguring horrors of the upland 'tree factories' and the blitzing of the agricultural landscape gave birth to the urban conservation lobby – powerful, articulate and angry. It was they who forced the forestry world to think before they planted, but by then a lot of damage had been done.

Afforestation is a very permanent thing, and before any activity takes place – clear felling, thinning, planting or underplanting – it is essential to think the plan right through and consider its effects on other possible uses of the forest besides timber production.

During the past thirty years many estate owners and farmers have played an invaluable role in preserving the landscape against the more extreme activities of commercial forestry and agriculture. Sport, whether shooting or fox hunting, has been an important incentive. Probably the single most worrying feature of recent agricultural activities, from the point of view of forestry, has been the wholesale destruction of small woodlands which are so valuable to many forms of wildlife, including game. Where there has been doubt in the mind of the fox-hunting farmer, it has nearly always been sport that has won the day and led to the preservation of these priceless assets. In addition, sporting landowners have planted a large number of new coverts on valuable low-ground farmland, something that commercial forestry could never justify on economic grounds. Though planted for pheasants, a multitude of other species – both flora and fauna – will take up residence in the new coverts. Few farmers or landowners will plant a spinney for a rare orchid or butterfly but many will do so for pheasants, and what suits the pheasant may well encourage the butterfly and orchid!

As you read this book, I hope it will become apparent that the needs of game management and forestry are not mutually exclusive and that game managers and foresters should not be opponents, but partners in today's enlightened approach to a broader use of land. My purpose in this book is to encourage game and wildlife managers and foresters to work closely together instead of meeting infrequently, in head-on collision!

1

The Changing Habitat

In the 1950s, when I first started work at Fordingbridge, the word 'habitat' – now much over-used – was virtually unknown for the simple reason that, both for game and wildlife in general, it existed in fair quantity and was not a problem. If a gamekeeper exercised good predator control and was blessed with fair weather during the breeding season, he could be reasonably sure of a good supply of wild game, whether pheasant, partridge or grouse, without resort to much more than a 'topping up' operation with reared birds.

The changing world of forestry, however, soon began to outstrip the expansive planting ideas of the past. During the Edwardian era and following World War I, attitudes to forestry planting were largely influenced by the grand landscape architects of an earlier age and the demands of gamekeepers employed to hold large quantities of reared pheasants. Advice on the layout of game coverts and the species recom-mended for planting gave no thought to expense or the needs of timber production. Management of established woodland was almost non-existent since imported timber was cheaper and of much better quality than home-grown timber and, in any case, woodland needed to be kept undisturbed in order to hold the birds.

Immediately after World War II, commercial forestry became all the rage, and the requirements of shooting were brushed aside as being frivolous and uneconomic. Apart from a very few landowners, commercial forestry on a significant scale had been largely confined to the Forestry Commission, set up in 1919. By 1950, therefore, it had only thirty years' experience to draw on, and stood in the same position as a young farmer in April, just after he has sown his first crop of wheat. In this situation, it is wise to borrow knowledge from those more experienced but, unfortunately for foresters, these could only be found outside Britain, and what works in the Black Forest does not neces-sarily apply to the ancient oak woods of Hampshire – and certainly looks very different!

The 1960s were therefore frustrating years for the game manager as the first effects of the early replantings began to be felt. Gamekeepers were faced with impenetrable jungles, gun-rides no longer wide enough to shoot in, bare-floored conifer plantations opened to the wind by brashing operations, and narrow, wet rides chewed and torn by the passage of heavy machinery.

Today, we must plan the habitat where once we took it for granted. Above all, we must assume that we are going to have to manage with but a fraction of the space formerly available, and for this reason our planning and design must be as efficient as possible.

I remember the shooting season 1961–2, and the bags of pheasants on three adjoining estates in East Anglia, totalling 5,600 hectares (14,000 acres). Only 5,000 pheasants were released which showed a return of just over 2,000 shot (all the birds being marked with wing tags). But the total bag for the season on the three shoots was 14,350 pheasants! There was also a fair bag of wild partridge, although the wild grey partridge was already in decline, and as an indicator of bird population trends in low-ground Britain this species has proved enormously important.

Packed into the Game Conservancy's computers there is now a mass of data going back a century or more to show how gamebird populations can react to changes in land use and none more dramatic and tragic than those which show the appalling effects of these changes during the past two decades. Just consider the scale of the problem in one small area of Britain, West Suffolk. Maps in 1837 showed a total wooded area of 2,900 hectares (7,200 acres) which had been reduced to 1,100 hectares (2,700 acres) by 1970. Broken down into size of woodland, the pattern of losses is as follows:

	No. of woodlands	
Woodland size	1837	1970
0–4ha (0–10 acres)	181	95
4–8ha (10–20 acres)	113	34
8–24ha (20–60 acres)	52	20
24–40ha (60–100 acres)	10	1
40+ ha (100+ acres)	11	4
Total	367	154

Today, there is some sign that the pendulum has come full swing, and may even be starting on its way back. In the past twenty years, shooting landowners have planted many thousands of hectares of woodland, most of it in the all-important small woodlands sector. Nor would a complete backward swing of the pendulum be desirable, since it could only come about as a result of a disastrous slump in the farming economy which even the most ardent conservationist must surely not want.

The value of small woodlands, as emphasised in chapter 2, lies in the importance of the woodland edge to game and wildlife. A 100m (110yd) square wood has 400m (440yd) of edge, but four 50m (55yd) square woods, covering the same total area, double the amount of woodland edge: 800m (880yd).

The pattern and distribution of woodland is equally important. Spinneys and coverts are the villages and towns of game and wildlife, and the hedges that connect them are the all-important roads. Destroy any of them and the population deteriorates in quality as well as quantity.

So when you are planning new planting of any kind, whether it is the corner of a field, a hedge or a 5ha (12 acre) covert, it is essential to consider the site in relation to the general habitat pattern of your farm or estate and not in isolation. For instance, for pheasants, it is just as important to consider their route into any new covert on foot as it is to estimate how they will fly out of it on a shooting day. (The question of siting will be discussed in more detail in chapter 3.)

Similarly, one must consider the effect on the landscape, not just after planting but in later years when the trees are at full height. Abrupt shapes must be softened and colours blended. The 'pyjama stripe' tree factories that cling to the sides of some of our loveliest hilly country are a constant reminder of that!

A tree crop takes a long time to grow and many social changes inevitably take place in that period. An oak wood planted in 1900 is now three-quarters of the way to being cropped, but during that time there has been a revolution in public access to the countryside. Most of the change has taken place in the past thirty years as a result of a vast increase in the standard of living, almost universal car ownership and increased leisure time for motoring.

Suppose the EEC imposed legislation allowing public access to all private woodland, as in most parts of West Germany, would you be prepared for it? Probably not, but there are ways in which you could avoid the worse effects of such legislation on your game coverts, for instance by attracting the public to one 'honey-pot' area which they would prefer – and where you might make some money out of them!

There are many possible ways of doing this and good planning should anticipate changes. Before you plant that old gravel pit, might it not be better left open and used to deaden the sound of scrambler cyclists, rather than have them roaring indiscriminately through the woods? Or, if you leave a 22m (25yd) margin unplanted around the lake, it will not only look nicer now (and make it easier to fish and establish wildfowl habitat), but it will enable you to put in a perimeter car park in the future if you have to.

Flexibility is essential in forest planning and if one includes the requirements of maximum game production, many of the features are

The Deer Hay Valley, the Manor Farm, Rockbourne, Hants. Designed for the late Sir Kynaston Studd Bt, this layout incorporates two new coverts shown on the left of the picture and the underplanting of the old oaks on the right. Pheasants are driven across guns standing in the deep valley between

dual purpose, particularly the actual *structure* of the coverts. The correct design of the edge is best for the adjoining farm; wide rides open up handsome vistas and give good access for timber extraction; the mixture of tree species desirable for gamebirds and other forms of wildlife will avoid the unattractive monotony of the tree factory; and make a more flexible marketing policy possible; and so on.

The need to keep sunshine on the floor of the forest for good game production requires a reasonably open tree canopy. This can help mitigate the cash flow problem of long-term forestry because it facilitates underplanting with short rotation crops such as Christmas trees, chestnut coppice for fencing material, ash coppice for firewood and small wood products, and large transplants for the landscape market.

The gamekeeper can also perform an important part of forest management in the control of forest pests, such as rabbits and squirrels, as well as his vital task of looking after the security side – few foresters are to be found in the woodlands after dark! Deer, too, must be kept under control for their own prosperity as well as that of the timber. As the Continental forester appreciates, they are a very valuable sporting asset which can make control self-financing or even profitable.

Any amount of advice is available on how to choose and plant trees and shrubs, but virtually none on how to design a wood for anything other than a straightforward commercial crop. The aim of this book is to enable the reader to design new plantings for game and wildlife as efficiently as possible. The old method of taking half a dozen hectares and planting them up 'with trees' will no longer suffice. The area to be planted will be trimmed down to the last square metre, the exact number of trees and shrubs must be known and the whole pattern must be purpose designed.

And, to my mind, the most essential feature to aim for is the ability to show good sporting pheasants. Numbers are not important, and all true sportsmen will prefer quality to quantity. There is nothing clever about killing a thousand or more pheasants in a day, but a great deal of skill is needed to put high fast pheasants over a team of guns in flat, featureless country.

Much goes into the making of a good day's shooting – the landscape; the skill of the gamekeeper; the meeting with old friends, whether guns or beaters; the efficiency of the pickers-up; the right proportions of steak and kidney in the lunchtime pie; and above all the way the birds are shown. They should be such that when a guest shoots one he is filled with pleasure at his skill. If each of your guests fires a hundred cartridges during the day and at the finish you can just muster enough pheasants to present them with a brace each then you have got the birds flying about right!

2
Designing a Pheasant Covert

THE WOODLAND EDGE

Pheasants are very much 'birds of the edge'. They will usually nest within a few metres of the outside of a wood or the side of a woodland ride. They will also nest on the edge of hedgerows and small patches of cover. Even in grass fields, most of the nests (usually found by the mower) are situated within 20m (22yd) of the perimeter. The most important sector of a good pheasant covert is therefore the edge. Its design and structure will largely determine its ability to produce a wild crop of pheasants in the summer and to hold birds during the winter – whether they are wild or hand-reared.

Where a wood adjoins a farm, one or other generally suffers. Farm crops compete for moisture and nutrients with the tree roots which, as a rough guide, extend as far as their branches. In addition, crops on a large area of adjoining land can be adversely affected by the shade from the trees, particularly on the north side of the wood. Those affected usually ripen later and involve the farmer in the considerable inconvenience of leaving a strip uncut at harvest time to return for a meagre yield two or three weeks later. Often this yield will not cover the cost of seed, cultivation, drilling, fertilising, spraying and harvesting. It cannot make financial sense to sacrifice the annual cash income from farm crops in favour of a distant and speculative income from timber.

On a farm in Essex the shade along the northern edge of a long and narrow 25ha (62 acre) wood on heavy land had rendered an area of almost 3ha (7.5 acres) incapable of being farmed economically. The illustration on pp. 16–17 shows the landowner's solution. The woodland edge was bulldozed to move the tree line back 20m (22yd) from the farm headland. The immediate effect was to bring back into cultivation 3ha (7.5 acres) of highly productive farmland and, incidentally, to provide two nesting edges for gamebirds where previously there had been one. In addition to pheasants, partridges (who dislike nesting under trees) now nest in the outer edge. If the edge is right for the farm it is also right for the game, always providing that shelter is included.

Let us now consider the design of a pheasant covert in more detail, although what follows is mostly concerned with basic *principles*. Figs 1–3 show that, taking the layout of the edge of the covert as an example, there is very considerable flexibility of choice in design within these principles. The other features which will be described share a similar variety of options.

(*pages 16–17*) This wide woodland edge, constructed to protect the neighbouring farm crop is ideal for game combining shelter with good nesting cover

In wintry conditions, warm sheltered coverts are essential to a good pheasant shoot and invaluable to many other animals as well

Protection from Wind

Pheasants dislike draughty woods, as do most other birds and animals. A well-designed covert must therefore provide shelter around its perimeter or, if it is on a steeply sloping site, islands of shelter within.

A pheasant spends all the daylight hours on the ground (and sometimes the night as well) and it is here that covert planting so often fails. Any new plantation will give good ground level shelter for about ten years or so and then quite suddenly, sometimes within a couple of seasons, the lower branches of the trees die off and the wind comes whistling in. Attempts at 'warming up' an existing wood by planting a few conifers around the outside have the same eventual result. The effect is to pull down the walls of the pheasant's house, leaving only a leaky roof.

Protection from wind must be provided at two levels. Ground level is the most important but some shelter is desirable in the roosting area, particularly in a small covert.

19

Fig 1 A simple woodland edge layout with windproof *Lonicera nitida* hedge and shelter belt of cypress. Three rows of trees for the shelter belt is a minimum, five or six would be better. The outside row would be felled at about 12 to 15 years

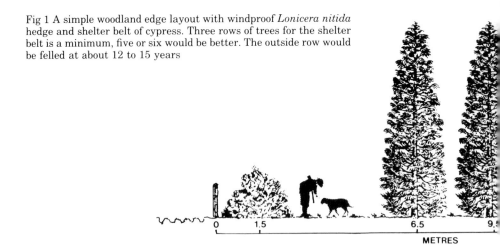

Fig 2 Woodland edge with windproof *Lonicera nitida* hedge and outside row of colourful medium height berry-bearing trees to soften the sombre effect of the cypress shelter belt

Fig 3 The most important sector of a good pheasant covert is the edge. Its design and structure will largely determine its ability to produce a wild 'crop' of pheasants in the summer and to hold birds during the winter, wild or hand-reared. Pheasants dislike draughty woods, particularly at ground level.

As the perimeter shelter belt of a covert grows older, the lower branches die away, particularly with species such as Scots pine. This allows the wind to enter between the top of the hedge and bottom of the tree canopy. Anticipate this by planting a row of laurel inside the shelter belt to fill the gap

.5　　　　　　14.5

This hedge of Lawson cypress is rapidly becoming ineffective as shelter because it has not been topped at 2m (6ft) as it should have been and cattle have been able to graze the lower edge and thus remove the most valuable feature, ground level wind shelter

The Perimeter Hedge

Good ground-level perimeter shelter is best provided by a hedge if the covert is on fairly flat ground. The hedge need be no more than head height but it *must* be windproof at all levels and particularly at the base. To achieve this, it is essential to plant it in the right position and manage it properly afterwards. Management these days must be mechanical and fast. The usual cause of deterioration in old woodland hedges is that they were planted close to the outside row of trees where mechanical management is impossible and where they are drawn up by the shade of the trees to form thin, straggly plants. They are then unsightly to look at and completely ineffective as shelter or as a means of excluding farm livestock.

The solution is to form a 'perimeter zone' inside the wood by leaving a space between the hedge and the first row of trees. When the covert is planted the perimeter zone needs to have a minimum width of 5m (16.5ft) to be effective and preferably 7m (23ft) (particularly on the north side).

The perimeter zone should ensure that the hedge remains in full sunlight where it will prosper, and that it can be easily maintained by a tractor running *inside* the wood. This last point is important because hedge maintenance is a winter job and a very high proportion of our cereal crops are now sown in the autumn which means that more often than not a tractor cannot work on the farm headland after October.

There is a good reason for the perimeter zone's generous dimensions. The outer row of trees, even if conifers, will eventually begin to throw a shadow over the farm headland and their branches will quickly overtop the hedge if it is planted close. It is essential to have a management programme whereby the outside rows of trees are progressively cropped in such a way that the wood is continually moving away from the farm headland until the trees reach their full height. This management should be self-financing otherwise it is unlikely to be carried out. For this reason, the outer row of trees must reach marketable size before they are cut as poles and this usually means a height of at least 5m (16.5ft). By this time their lower branches and the side growth of the hedge will have reduced the width of the perimeter zone to a couple of metres or less and there must still be room for a tractor to pass through.

The perimeter zone, if well designed, will give the following advantages:

1. The tree line will be kept away from the farm headland.
2. There will be access for the hedge to be trimmed from inside the wood.
3. If there is a boundary ditch, it will remain free of tree roots and leaves and can easily be cleaned out mechanically, again from inside the wood.

An old hardwood stand invading the farm headland. The author is standing (right) by the original fence line.

4. The unplanted space will provide nesting cover for both pheasants and partridges, and can easily be kept trimmed to avoid excessive growth by colonising shrubs.
5. In the early life of the wood the space can be used to grow a profitable crop of Christmas trees.

I hesitated over this last point because so often I have included some Norway spruce for this purpose only to find that no one bothers to harvest them and they grow up to eliminate the perimeter zone completely. However, today's estates and farms are keen to seek income wherever possible, and a well-managed and marketed crop of Christmas trees in the perimeter zone of a new plantation could pay for the considerable expense of a perimeter fence and rabbit netting. But please do not leave any unsold trees to grow on!

Shelter Hedge Species

The best stockproof hedge plant has always been hawthorn. It is also very handsome, can produce a useful crop of berries and is native to this country. It should be planted in a double row with 30cm (12in) between the plants and 20cm (8in) between the rows which should be staggered. For the hedge to be stockproof and reasonably windproof, it should be cut and laid about six or seven years after planting and thereafter trimmed annually and kept to a height not exceeding 2m (6.5ft).

This form of upkeep was simple in bygone days when there was plenty of available labour, but it is not so easy today. Any form of management that does not eventually result in income is extremely unpopular and often results in neglect. Although hawthorn can produce berries which are a useful source of winter food for many species of birds and small rodents, as well as gamebirds, very few are produced on a well-trimmed hedge. For a good crop of berries it is better to allow some thorns to grow on as small trees inside the wood. Even when meticulously managed, a hawthorn hedge does not give particularly good shelter from wind once its leaves have fallen unless it is very wide and intermingled with brambles, dead grasses, nettles and bracken. This type of hedge, often found around very old wood-lands, is excellent and can be very colourful in the autumn if it includes a mixture of species such as field maple, guelder rose, the wayfarer tree and dog rose. But to be effective it must be wide and dense and, apart from the rabbit problem this can produce, such a hedge is expensive to establish and manage.

For a good windproof hedge an evergreen species such as the shrub honeysuckle, *Lonicera nitida* is ideal. The advantages of *Lonicera* are as follows:

- it is evergreen and absolutely windproof;
- if left untrimmed it remains at a height of 2–3m (6–10ft) and therefore needs no management;
- it does not spread by seeds and only suckers occasionally;
- it is unpalatable and, even when newly planted, is rarely eaten by rabbits, hares or deer;
- it is very easily grown from cuttings without the need of artificial heat or expensive rooting compounds;
- if you buy shrewdly the plants are only a little more expensive than hawthorn but you only need one-third of the number in a hedge.

Its disadvantages are:

- it does not prosper under shade;
- it is not stockproof;
- it is inconsistent in growth on exposed, low temperature sites;
- it produces no berries.

Lonicera is not a native plant (it was introduced to Britain from West China in 1908), but I have no hesitation in recommending it as shelter because it is vastly superior to native species such as hawthorn. All our native species of flora and fauna benefit by protection from exposure, and if this is best provided by a non-native species, occupying a very small proportion of the area and requiring no expensive management, then that species must be the most sensible choice.

The author in a young plantation showing the gap between the *Lonicera nitida* hedge and the Scots pine perimeter belt

The correct way to plant *Lonicera nitida* using thick slices of very wet straw to mulch the plants and reduce competition from weed growth

When planting *Lonicera* it is worth going to some trouble to ensure success. It does not like being out of the ground too long and a journey of more than twenty-four hours, particularly if tightly packed, can cause heavy casualties. If you have to buy in plants it is well worth while arranging to have them lifted in the morning, collect them in the afternoon and plant them next day.

To achieve a high success rate in establishment, mulch the plants to retain moisture and, above all, to suppress competitive weed growth. This is not difficult, but it does require planning ahead. Use well-saturated straw for the purpose. Place straw bales around the line of the hedge (one bale per four plants) after the cereal harvest, assuming that planting is to take place in the following January or February (*never* plant *Lonicera* after the new growth has started, usually in early March). By this time the bales are soaked right through and virtually immovable – hence the importance of putting them in place and not stacking them.

The easiest way to plant *Lonicera* is first to run round the line of the hedge with a plough. The plants can be placed in the open furrow and the loose earth pulled back around them. A single row of plants 1m (3ft) apart is sufficient. Where the site is grassed over it is best to kill this out well beforehand with a suitable non-residual spray. As you plant, place a generous slice of straw – 15cm (6in) or so thick – flat on each side of the shrub and a single slice between, treading them down firmly as you do so. If you can repeat the application of straw twelve months after planting this will be beneficial, although farmyard manure is even better.

Without a straw mulch, losses can be fairly high with all the resulting additional labour and expense. *Lonicera* tends to produce a poor rather straggly growth if forced to compete with a mass of weeds, particularly tall grass.

I have seen *Lonicera* hedges prospering at high altitudes in the north of Scotland but these may be exceptions. In Germany and Denmark, *Lonicera nitida* is thought to be insufficiently hardy to survive their winters and nurserymen there recommend *Lonicera pileata* which certainly seems to survive well but tends to be low growing. I can see no reason why *pileata* should be more hardy than *nitida*, but for difficult exposed sites a mixture of hawthorn and ramanas rose plants spaced 1m (3ft) apart, with *Lonicera nitida* between each plant would be advisable. The thorn and rose will strengthen the structure of the hedge to withstand the weight of snow and the *Lonicera* will provide a reasonable evergreen content to make it more windproof. Occasional trimming will be necessary to prevent the thorn growing too tall, about once every three to five years according to growth. If this is impracticable because of the site then the thorn must be left out of this mixture.

The ramanas rose was introduced from north-east Asia in 1796. The native dog rose would not be suitable for our purpose since it is not so dense in structure as ramanas, but I would include a few because they are such beautiful plants. If plants could be made available in quantity, the pea tree (see p. 163) might be used in exposed situations as a substitute for *Lonicera* or thorn. It is used extensively as a snow break alongside the highways in North America and Canada.

Tree Hedge Species

Many trees can be trimmed to form efficient windproof hedges. Lawson cypress, Sitka spruce, Norway spruce, western red cedar, Scots pine, lodgepole pine – all have been used successfully. I have seen excellent hedges of Sitka in exposed sites.

Nevertheless, all tree hedges have one considerable disadvantage in that they *must* be topped at 2–3m (6–10ft) and kept at that height. If this is not done they gradually become bare at ground level and the wind comes in at the worst point for pheasants (see photograph on p.22).

People are frequently reluctant to cut tree hedges at the right time. It is always 'next year' until the gamekeeper complains of a draught around his feet and then it is too late. It is surprising how suddenly this occurs, particularly in narrow shelter belts. Tree hedges can deteriorate from excellent winter holding capacity to virtually nil in two seasons. For this reason I would only recommend trees for hedging as a last resort.

High Shelter

Although a perimeter hedge is importance for ground-level shelter at the extreme edge of a game covert, its effect will only be local and general wind protection to the whole woodland area must also be provided. In steep sloping sites this is vital, and additional contour shelter belts may be necessary (see Fig 19 on p. 91).

First, though, the level site. A tall conifer shelter belt should be planted inside the perimeter zone and, as with tree hedges, there is a considerable choice of available species but the best are Leyland cypress (particularly for speed of growth), Lawson cypress and western red cedar. All have a fairly narrow branching habit and reduce the effect of shade on the perimeter zone. Other good species would be Norway or Sitka spruce and western hemlock. The pines tend to be less suitable and are quick to open up at ground level.

Given a reasonable-sized game covert – at least 200m (220yd) square – it is important to have enough tree lines in the perimeter belt to allow for the removal of an outside row or two to keep the shade away

Large straw bales can be used to provide temporary edge shelter but they also tend to harbour pests, particularly rats

from the farm headland. Five rows at 2.5m (8ft) spacing would be ideal. At about fifteen years the outside row can be removed, and the next if necessary at about twenty years, although some care must be taken in deciding on the second row if there is a danger of windblow. The north side is the most likely to cause shading problems and if it is necessary to reduce the number of rows due to lack of space on a small site then priority for the maximum number must go to the northern edge.

A continuous edge of conifers is rather monotonous, but this can be modified by including a colour screen of contrasting species. Individual trees or groups of trees can be planted at irregular intervals outside the conifers and larger groups could penetrate further leaving only one or two conifer rows inside them.

For this purpose, given suitable soil, the *Sorbus* family, such as mountain ash, common whitebeam and Swedish whitebeam, is a good choice. Apart from their attractive appearance, they produce berries that are eaten by pheasants and many songbirds and, being of medium size at maturity, they are unlikely to intrude significantly on the perimeter zone or farm headland. A few larch can also be used to vary the colour and soften the unsympathetic appearance of a conifer belt.

A further refinement to the design of the woodland edge would be to include common laurel. Again, it is a dull plant to look at and so it could be planted as a substitute for the *inside* row of conifers (see Fig 3 on pp. 20–1). It will be invaluable as the latter grow to maturity and become open to the wind below their live branch line. Laurel can grow to 6m (20ft) or more and will usefully fill in this gap as we shall see later in connection with shelter belts (see chapter 4). If they become too tall they can be cut to the ground and will quickly regenerate.

Another useful species for this purpose is the *Malus* family of crab apples, and *floribunda* is a favourite of mine with its small fruits which are readily eaten by pheasants. The wild cherry or gean is a handsome tree but is inclined to become rather too large. However, it has a very lightly branched crown and throws the minimum amount of shade. Another member of the *Prunus* family which can be useful is *cerasifera* or the cherry plum whose fruits can be excellent for human consumption (providing you include at least their own weight of sugar when cooking!). A good colour contrast can be achieved with the beautiful golden autumn leaves of field maple.

The edge of a new woodland should be given a great amount of thought in the planning, whether it is to be specifically planted as a game covert or purely for commercial timber production. The correct design will have a significant effect on the shooting potential and the farm economy. Further, it is the part of the woodland that you see most often and its effect on the surrounding landscape should be very carefully considered.

BREEDING AND HOLDING COVER

Breeding cover is low ground vegetation which must be sheltered from wind and not too dense. Holding cover is similar but with the addition of warm and sheltered night roosting. Pheasants do not live in dense cover but they need it close by for three reasons:

- as a source of food from the seeds and fruits of the plants that grow there;
- as a light protective screen for their nests;
- as a refuge if they are disturbed or threatened.

If the woodland is very bare on the ground, the most common cause is a dense tree or coppice canopy preventing sufficient natural or introduced ground cover to grow. Too little light will leave the ground bare, as in a mature beech or spruce wood, and too much can produce an impenetrable jungle, particularly where brambles are present. The treatment of bare floors in mature woodland is dealt with in chapter 6, 'Woodland Rehabilitation'; the following discussion will centre on prevention rather than cure.

Two shrubs which will tolerate exceptionally heavy shade are common laurel and box, but they cannot be *established* under these conditions. They must be planted before the tree canopy closes. Planning is therefore all important to avoid the common problem in a new plantation usually summed up by the keeper as 'too thick at the start and too thin at the end'. When replanting clear-felled woodland, the very thick initial growth of ground vegetation, particularly brambles and coppice is partly overcome in the first five years or so by the forester's normal weeding programme. The next five years in softwood, and up to ten in hardwood, can be very difficult. Some of the excessive growth can be suppressed if the initial planting is carried out under dappled shade thrown by a thin stock of trees left from the previous crop, or by spraying with a brushwood killer before replanting. When planting is carried out on virgin ground grass weeds are another problem. Though not impenetrable, like brambles, they are sufficiently dense and wet in winter to discourage pheasants.

The weed problem of young plantations today is often solved by wide spacing between the rows, allowing access for mechanical control. Unfortunately, this is not always practicable in replanting schemes where the stumps from the previous crop are a hazard to machinery, or where the site is too steep or rocky to use it, but chemical control between the rows can have the same effect (see chapter 7 on weeding).

Where undergrowth is very thick, pheasants will tend to use only the fringe for nesting and bury themselves in it out of reach of beaters on a shooting day. A number of tracks cut through the undergrowth will produce more edge and give a much greater choice of nesting sites. The keeper will also be able to feed along the tracks and use them for controlling predators, beaters will be able to work properly, and the forester can see what is happening to the young trees.

When the tree canopy closes, the problem is to get enough ground cover evenly distributed through the wood. This is why the pure conifer plantation is so difficult because all the cover tends to be concentrated in the perimeter zone and ride sides. In such a situation nesting birds are far more vulnerable to predators because only a limited area of cover has to be hunted by their enemies. Even under pines and larches, where cover often grows well, the coldness of a conifer wood discourages pheasants from nesting anywhere except at the extreme edge.

Nevertheless, some cover is essential for holding pheasants during the shooting season. Pines and larches often go through a period when all ground cover disappears and then recolonises as the canopy grows higher and less dense after thinning. To avoid this gap, it is necessary to plant with shade-bearing species before the canopy first closes, ie

Wide rides make a handsome addition to woodlands and provide valuable edge for breeding pheasants. When making new rides in old woodlands some good specimen trees should always be retained

when planting the trees. There is no better species for this purpose than common laurel which, when established, will live happily beneath pines, larches and even beech. It is easily managed and reasonably accessible for beaters. Box will do the same but is such a very slow grower that it tries the patience of most people and, since it is much smaller, needs to be planted in far greater numbers than laurel. This makes it more expensive but since it is a handsome plant it is always a good idea to include a few. The planting of ground cover in new plantations is discussed in more detail in chapter 9. Whatever you do, please avoid that menace to the forester and shoot manager *Rhododendron ponticum*. On acid soil in a mild climate it can swamp a woodland and render it impenetrable.

Drainage is also very important. Although some pheasant species are quite at home in the marshes and reed beds of Central Asia, cold damp woodland does not produce the right type of cover, and is fatal to young chicks. Impeded drainage also predisposes the area to windblow.

Adequate ground cover will nearly always grow naturally given sufficient sunlight and drainage, but the correct amount can only be expected for a proportion of the life of a wood. Some provision must be made for the lean years. A good pattern of rides (including the perimeter zone) and judicious planting of shrubs can go a long way towards solving this problem and is particularly important when planting on new ground where colonisation by natural shrub species, principally hawthorn and brambles, can take many years. You may even need to plant a few groups of brambles! They are the most common shrub species in all the best game coverts.

THE PLANNING AND CONSTRUCTION OF RIDES

In order to be able to design the correct pattern of rides, it is essential to understand their purpose clearly. For the forester, rides are important for the following reasons:

- for inspecting the growing trees;
- for extracting and stacking thinnings;
- for the removal of large trees;
- as firebreaks.

The game manager needs them for different reasons:

- to provide additional territorial and nesting edge for pheasants (as well as many other bird species);
- as sunning areas for broods of chicks or as part of a release pen;
- to harbour insects for chicks;
- for access and winter feeding;
- for controlling beaters, especially in a young plantation;

33

- for flushing pheasants;
- for standing guns (particularly in large woodlands);
- for controlling predators and rabbits;
- for controlling deer.

The Forestry Commission appears to plan the ride structure adequately in the smaller woodland areas, but private woodland owners and contractors seem to ignore the problem except in large tree factories. Planting a sizeable wood without making rides is like building a factory without doors! It is surprising how many forestry 'plans of operations' have anything other than a purely perfunctory extraction plan. An example of this was a 15ha (37 acre) wood of fine oaks which was clear-felled and replanted with pure stands of larch and Douglas fir with not even a pedestrian track between the compartments. When the new owner tried to plan the shooting, it was necessary to bring in a bulldozer to make new rides at very considerable expense. Subsequent thinning would have been impossible without them and it could have been a nightmare to drive on a shooting day.

In large woodlands, wide hard-surfaced rides are essential for timber extraction

Narrow tracks such as this are sunless in summer, damp all the year, and cut up into a quagmire if used by vehicles

In a small covert, the best system is to base the plan on one large central ride with radiating subsidiary tracks. This central ride should be at least 20m (22yd) wide. Although this may sound excessive, there is a sound reason behind it. It might be suggested that it is better to leave a narrow track when planting and widen it when the first thinning takes place. Long experience has taught me, however, that this is extremely unlikely to happen. Once a tree is growing well it has a value and foresters, land agents and accountants will bully you mercilessly if you threaten to cut it down during your lifetime! And even if you are tough enough to fend off their finger-waggings, you will only have a ride covered in stumps which will make it extremely difficult to manage. The money you get from the sale of the young trees will not cover the cost of hiring a bulldozer.

Norway spruce as Christmas trees can help to make it economic for the forester. When establishing a plantation, a 2.5m (8ft) track should first be levelled and grassed down in the 20m (22yd) ride. The remaining area can be planted with ten rows of Christmas trees. If well managed, the income from these trees can make a very useful contribution to establishment costs. Two or three crops could be grown.

So-called 'instant trees' for the landscape market could be another possible source of income. These can be very profitable, always providing that the marketing and management is professionally carried out. Choice of species is important and the current trends in the market should be studied before planting. At present, the most popular ones are maple, cherry, horse chestnut, lime, silver birch, common ash, mountain ash, common whitebeam, alder, standard thorn, crab apple and London plane.

The object is to produce heavy-headed standards, usually in the 3–4m (9–13ft) range, with straight clean stems. The trees should be planted in peat to encourage good fibrous roots which can withstand the shock of transplanting. Side branches should be removed from the stems and the roots pruned two or three years after planting and again the year before lifting. When planting, space the trees 4m (13ft) apart. The time for growth to marketable size from plants 1m (3ft) high varies with the species and soil, but it is usually five to ten years.

It should be emphasised again, however, how important it is to grow these trees properly if you are to find a ready market. Too often they are badly grown by amateurs and then sold off cheaply to the less scrupulous retailers. Better to approach a good nursery and negotiate a contract with them which would include competent supervision.

The management of rides is just as important as their planning. They are often left for years in young plantations with little attention and this can result in a gradual invasion of unwanted species such as coppice from old tree stumps or self-seeded thorn, sycamore and birch. Eventually an expensive clearing operation is required. Even on virgin ground it is important to see that the rides do not become a jungle of brambles and thistles. They should be levelled, cultivated and sown with grass which will ensure rapid and cheap maintenance with ordinary tractor-drawn farm equipment.

Maintenance is simply a matter of mowing the grass once or twice a year, but it is best to leave an infrequently cut marginal strip 2–3m (6–9ft) wide on each side of the ride. This will provide nesting cover for pheasants and some food for deer. If this edge strip is colonised by brambles so much the better, but coppice or tree seedlings must be regularly cut back or killed.

When making new rides during a replanting operation, growth from old coppice stools and young shoots from tree stumps can be killed off with a chemical brushwood killer. Subsequent management can be difficult if there are large numbers of tree stumps combined with uneven ground, and a bulldozer is usually the only practical answer.

Other points to watch when planning rides are drainage and wind. Drainage is important, particularly on heavy soils and peat. Without

Narrow tracks and footpaths soon become overgrown and of no value to either the game manager or the forester

it, the rides are quickly cut up by the passage of vehicles and tend to foster a rank growth of vegetation which can become a fire risk in late winter and spring. Deep ditches with steep sides should be avoided because they are potential death traps for young pheasants. Steep sides erode quickly and soon render the ditch ineffective unless it is dug out again. The aim should be wide ditches with gently sloping sides. Ride side ditches can be ineffective on heavy soil, leaving the centre of the ride undrained. By far the best answer is to construct the ride with a pronounced camber – 1.25m (4ft) should not be too much on a 20m (22yd) width – allowing a wide, shallow drainage ditch on each side. With no steep banks to cave in, this ditch will require little maintenance and will not trap pheasant chicks.

Square cut drainage ditches make death traps for pheasant chicks and eventually erode and thus become ineffective for drainage unless re-excavated. Ditch bank slopes should be no steeper than 45° and preferably much less

A well cambered ride eliminates the need for difficult-to-maintain marginal drainage ditches. Dry rides are good for young pheasant broods

Wind should never be allowed to blow directly into a ride. Access to a wood should always be made at an angle to avoid this (see Fig 11 on pp. 70–1). Where an existing ride opens straight into a wood, a new access should be cut through at an angle. The old entrance should be blocked off by planting a small group of quick-growing conifers behind a wall of straw bales to give temporary shelter. The very large bales are ideal for this purpose and will last long enough for the trees to grow well above them. Rides which are 20m (22yd) wide can also be draughty if they are over 100m (110yd) long, even where the ends are blocked. Curving the ride is the best answer, but another solution is to create

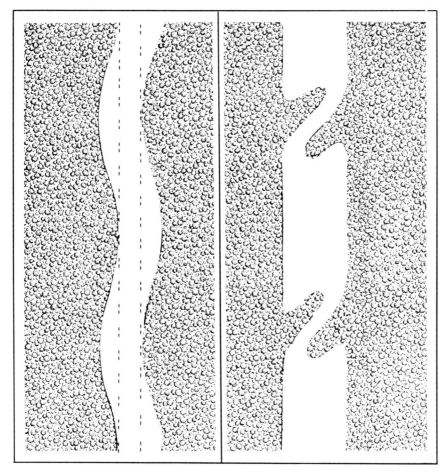

Fig 4 When opening up an old ride (shown with dotted lines) curves will lessen the effect of wind and provide better cock pheasant territories

Fig 5 Wind baffles are valuable in straight wide rides and are not difficult to plant. Lawson cypress, Leyland cypress or *Thuja* are suitable species

wind baffles by planting groups of conifers every 50m (55yd) or so, leaving a central gap for access (see Figs 4 and 5, p. 39). An additional reason for avoiding long straight rides which are open to roads or public footpaths is that any passing poacher can assess the pheasant situation at a glance without entering the wood.

NEW RIDES IN OLD WOODLAND

It is a reasonably simple operation to make new rides in an old broad-leaved covert but less so in conifers where windblow may result. My method in old woodland is very often self-financing and only removes a proportion of the timber crop. They are not really rides in the true sense but they make very handsome vistas through a big wood, especially when slightly curved.

The procedure is simple. First mark the *centre* line of the new ride with twine fastened at waist height to convenient trees or posts driven into the ground. Next mark the trees that are going to be left standing.

Rides for flushing pheasants or separating pheasant drives can easily be made without felling too many trees

They should, of course, be good specimens and of mixed age: some nearly mature, some 5–7m (16–23ft) high. If the wood is poorly stocked with quality trees then some may have to be planted. The canopy from the trees left standing should only cover about a quarter to a third of the ride. Be generous in the number of large trees you mark because when the others are felled you can look at them again and take out a few more if necessary – you cannot put any back! When the preparatory work is completed, the felling can be carried out. Assuming that you are going to make the ride 30m (33yd) wide, then you must clear fell every tree and shrub *as near to ground level as possible* for 15m (16.5yd) on either side of the line you have marked, leaving only the trees you have decided to retain. Make sure that all lop and top from the felling and any old dead branches or trees lying on the ground are removed or burned. It is essential to leave the ground as bare as possible so that it can be cut over regularly with a tractor-mounted brush cutter. This should be done in September each year, and if possible in March or April as well. A strip, 2–3m (6–10ft) wide, should be left infrequently cut at the side of the ride to allow nesting and holding cover to grow as previously described.

Rides such as these can be used for many purposes: for standing guns or flushing birds; for dividing a big wood into conveniently sized pheasant drives; for controlling deer; for timber extraction; for inclusion as a sunning area in a release pen; and so on. They also make very attractive features in a wood since they can open up handsome vistas, particularly if they follow a stream or a valley. When a big wood is regularly drawn by hounds these wide rides make viewing much easier and damage by horses is reduced to a minimum.

CHOICE OF TREE SPECIES

The choice of tree species is undoubtedly at the centre of most arguments between forester and game manager. The old-fashioned hardwood with regularly coppiced hazel underwood and a few conifers for roosting were ideal for game and wildlife. This type of woodland was very long-lived and produced a continuous succession of all types and densities of undergrowth as the compartments of hazel were regularly cropped. Many of these magnificent game coverts have now disappeared under a carpet of conifers, often of indifferent quality.

Britain's timber stocks had indeed been run down to a dangerously low level by 1945 and drastic action was needed, but the two factors

---

(*overleaf*) A good distribution of safe nesting cover is an essential feature of a pheasant covert (*T. H. Blank*)

that seem to dominate modern forestry planning are that 80 per cent of our timber requirements are for softwood and that hardwood takes much longer to grow. Even if all the available land in Britain were afforested we could only produce less than 10 per cent of our total requirements and we would be just as short of hardwoods as softwoods. It takes twice as long to grow an oak as it does a Scots pine but it still takes a very long time to grow a Scots pine! The time scale in forestry makes long-term planning a nightmare and the economics pure dreamland. A farmer attempts to predict with reasonable accuracy his profits on a crop which takes him a few months to grow. He is frequently wrong. And yet the forester seems to cheerfully predict the financial return on crops which take a minimum of forty years to grow, and more often than not, two or three times that length of time.

Nevertheless, the 'short' rotation of conifers tends to be much more attractive to investors than the longer term for hardwoods. There is no doubt that this makes sense in the high rainfall 'tree factory' areas of the north and west which are, incidentally, the least productive for gamebirds. In the south and east, however, the choice should be different. Farming is much more important than forestry and the dense human population stimulates a constantly increasing demand for amenity – both passive, as seen through the windscreen of a motor car, and active, as enjoyed by the sportsman or walker. And here the old-fashioned English *mixed* woodland is so much more attractive than the conifer forest – with its mile upon mile of telegraph poles with green tufts stuck on top! A forester's dream, perhaps, but no more attractive as a landscape feature than the chimneys of a brickworks or a row of electricity pylons.

The scale of forestry in the south and east of Britain is also very much smaller and more fragmented than elsewhere. The comparatively small compact woodlands have excellent access to good roads and extraction is rarely a problem. In addition the market is close, specialised and varied, demanding timber for every purpose from the crafts of wood carving and marquetry to the oak panelling for the doors of a city hall. This should lead to much greater flexibility so that small parcels of timber and even individual specimen trees could be marketed as they reach maturity avoiding the large clear fellings which are necessary in the tree factories, and the economic pitfalls of monoculture and single-purpose crops.

The private woodland owner has a big advantage where mixed species woodlands are concerned and yet there still tends to be a leaning towards 'mini-forests' of conifers in imitation of the large producer. It should be remembered that Britain still has an annual requirement of 250 million cubic feet of hardwoods, of which 200

No ground cover will grow in a wood like this unless the canopy shade is broken, usually impractical at this stage

million have to be imported. It is here that the small woodland owner's market could lie. Much of the difficulty of selling hardwoods in the past has been caused by a preponderance of bad timber resulting from neglect many years ago. Matters are very different now: knowledge-able and efficient forestry management should be the rule rather than the exception. Softwoods may always be the 'bread and butter' of the forestry industry, but there seems to be no reason why the traditional hardwood areas of Great Britain should not continue to grow a fair proportion of our most handsome deciduous trees. Certainly, from the aesthetic point of view, no one wants to see our woodlands turned into a 'poor man's Scandinavia'.

A good mixture of species is the aim of the game manager and a good balance would be had with 60 per cent softwood and 40 per cent hardwood at the start, with the hardwood to form the final crop. A 'chessboard' pattern of hardwood groups in a softwood matrix is preferable to ordinary line planting. The choice of the softwood species is important. Wherever possible, pines and larches should be planted since they allow a fair amount of undergrowth while nearly all the other conifers, such as the spruces, firs and cypresses, produce a completely bare floor. (It is the increased use of spruce as opposed to native pine – with the consequent lack of undergrowth – that is making our northern forest less and less attractive for capercaillie.)

Of course, there are some areas where the soil and climate rule out any species other than conifers. However, if the general principles that have been set out – hedge, perimeter zone, wide rides and well-designed flushing points – are incorporated in the woodland plan, even pure conifer woods can be made reasonably productive for pheasants. The game food bill will always be heavier, and the stock of breeding birds and their breeding success lower in conifer woods, but supplementary food requirements will be reduced in direct proportion to the amount of sunlight that is admitted. More sun means more growth of natural food and cover plants. A dense canopy of conifers, particularly spruce, can reduce the ground temperature by as much as 10°F (5.6°C) compared to hardwoods. Warmth thus becomes a vital factor. For this

Laurel growing well beneath the shade of these thirty-year-old pines and larches makes excellent ground cover

Box growing beneath a dense beech canopy. Note how there is no other vegetation on the ground

reason, a draught-excluding hedge or stone wall is of great importance in a pure conifer wood. However, it must not be thought that hardwoods cannot cause problems where ground cover is concerned. In pure even-aged stands, oak, ash and sycamore can almost eliminate undergrowth if they are not thinned to reduce the density of the canopy. Beech is certainly the most difficult species in this respect because it is not only the tree canopy that inhibits the growth of ground cover but the massive accumulation of very slow-rotting fallen leaves. This problem is often accentuated by excessive alkalinity in the soil, making beech the only suitable hardwood species to grow. The only answer to this problem is to underplant with laurel or box before the canopy closes. If you already have a semi-mature beech wood then there is nothing you can do because it would require excessive and very uneconomic thinning to open the canopy sufficiently to promote the growth of natural ground cover.

The choice of tree species will be restricted by local conditions of soil, climate and site aspect but there will usually be a number to choose from except in the case of extreme site conditions. Chapter 9 discusses the selection of tree and shrub species in more detail.

To sum up, the basic features which should be incorporated into the design of good pheasant covert are as follows:

- protection from wind;
- breeding cover for the production of wild pheasants;
- holding cover to retain both wild and reared birds in wintertime;
- a well-planned layout of rides and feed tracks;
- provision for flushing pheasants on a shooting day encouraging them to fly high and fast over a team of guns.

3

Planning
for the Shooting Day

THE FLIGHT OF A PHEASANT

Before one begins to plan the features for showing fast, sporting pheasants on a shooting day, it is useful to have a knowledge of some of their physical peculiarities and flying habits.

First, consider the bird as it appears on the carving dish. It has a plump breast and two fine legs and thighs, but the wings are barely worth considering as anything but a rather poor 'second helping'. Do not be deceived by this: the muscles in the wings are only there to stretch them out, and twist them about, the real driving power comes from the big muscles of the breast. A pheasant can fly quite long distances if it has to but it is the *way* in which it flies that is so important. It does so in short bursts of power, gliding in between, and this is common to all game birds such as partridges and grouse. The physiology of the breast muscle is designed to give great power but only for a short time, rather in the way that a cheetah can accelerate to a great speed over a short distance but then, if it has not caught its prey, quickly fades away.

The most important thing to remember is the length of time for which the pheasant can maintain the *initial* burst of power as it takes off and this is approximately eight seconds. When flying from low cover, such as a game crop, it is surprising how far it can go in such a short time: 140m (154yd) if the average speed is 35mph (55kph) varying, of course, with the wind speed. In flat country, assuming that it has achieved a reasonable height during this initial burst of energy, it will fly for a few seconds more before commencing its descent. The trajectory resembles that of a rifle bullet with a gentle incline to a peak, followed by a rapidly increasing angle of descent.

The art of showing good pheasants is to place the guns beneath the point where the birds reach their maximum height and speed. It may sound simple, but there are other very important features to be borne in mind. First of all, remember those splendid legs and thighs! A

pheasant is a strong, fast runner and it does not do so in short bursts but can keep going continuously for some time. It will always prefer to run and rarely flies except when forced to. There is also no doubt that it uses a tremendous amount of its energy resource when it does have to fly. For this reason alone you must never expect it to fly more than once in an hour; you may force it to do so but it will be a poor bird to show to the guns. The planning of a day's shooting, particularly where return drives are concerned, must always bear this in mind. For instance, it is common practice to spend the morning driving pheasants away from their home coverts (such as release points) and then giving them an hour's rest during lunch before driving them 'home'. This works well if there are enough drivers available but one can face the problem of having to eat two or three lunches if it is to be made to work!

Next, consider what happens to the bird *before* it takes wing. If it has run a long way and been harried by dogs and over-excited beaters, it will be in a state of panic and will often bury itself in thick cover from which it needs a very considerable drain on its reserves of energy to break free. Almost as bad is the use of wire netting to flush the birds. They can be seen banging their heads against it, often for quite a considerable time, before flushing – usually in a panicky crowd of other birds.

Then there is the matter of what the bird encounters immediately after it takes wing. If it has to scramble and fight its way up through thick tree or shrub cover half the precious eight seconds and considerably more than half its reserves of strength can be used up by the time it gets clear.

Watching pheasants move in front of a good team of beaters under a skilled gamekeeper, it can be seen that they are not particularly worried and will usually amble along quite slowly if there are patches of cover on their way. In bare-floored woodland they will move quicker but still not fast enough to use much energy. Whether they take cover early in the drive or run right on, they should not be greatly alarmed until the beaters (or well-disciplined dogs) are right on them when they should rocket from the ground in one explosive burst of adrenalin-powered energy. Thereafter, they should have a reasonably uninterrupted flight at an angle of between $25°$ and $35°$ if they are to attain their maximum speed before leaving the covert. All being well, their first sight of the gun-line will catch them at this point, flying fast and with two or three seconds of full power still available to lift them high over the guns. Even so, in flat terrain it will be an exceptional bird

(left) Flushed from high ground well forward of the guns, this pheasant is a test for any good sportsman *(John Tarlton)*

A valley bottom, cleared of all except a few trees, makes a fine gunstand to show high pheasants

which achieves a height in excess of 25m (80ft) unless lifted by a strong wind. Without a static feature such as a tree to use as a comparison, people often have a very exaggerated idea of the height of a bird flying across open country. But how many times have you seen a pheasant fly above the larger type of electric pylon which is about 40m (130ft) in height? It is rare even to see one fly over the sagging wire in between, which is about 35m (115ft) above the ground at its lowest point in winter. Undulating land is therefore invaluable since it can enable you to place the guns on low ground to increase the range rather than trying to make the birds fly higher.

Pheasants driven inside large woodlands will climb over the trees if the tree canopy is reasonably open and they are flushed well away from the guns. Once above the trees, however, there is no reason for them to fly higher until they see the guns. Even if the gun-ride is 50m (55yd) wide the birds will only have time to lift a few metres after seeing the guns and before crossing them. Again, undulating country is invaluable if it enables you to have gunstands in valley bottoms and flushing points well up on higher ground. But do not let the forester bully you into growing, say, poplars in the 'wasted areas' (his term) of gunstands. Your guests will only shoot the leaders out of the trees which will irritate the forester even further!

THE SITING AND DESIGN OF FLUSHING POINTS

If coverts have a reasonably open canopy then pheasants can be expected to flush from almost any point of a drive. This is particularly so where there is a fairly good stock of wild birds. Nevertheless, there are always those who run forward and will only stop when they see the guns. Even this will not necessarily make them fly in the right direction. They may break back over the beaters after hearing the shooting at close quarters or work their way round the flanks of the gun-line and sneak past along a hedge or ditch if nobody is situated there to stop them.

A flushing point must therefore be sited to collect these pedestrians at a suitable distance in front of the gunstand and allow the beaters to flush them *before* they have seen the guns. There is nothing worse than having birds flush at your feet in a woodland ride. Almost as bad is to see them run out of the edge of the covert and then potter up and down in front of the guns like so many barnyard fowls.

These pheasants, flushing too close to the guns, are low and slow. The sewelling is behind the guns whereas it should have been well in front of them! (*John Tarlton*)

Sewelling can be very effective in preventing pheasants from running too far forward on a shooting day. It must always be sited in the open so that pheasants can see it well ahead of them. (*right*) A man jerking the sewelling encourages the pheasants to rise well before they reach it

Ideally, birds should take wing at least 40m (44yd) from the line of the guns because, even where the latter are standing down in a deep valley, you must still give the birds room to accelerate to their maximum speed. Remember that large, fat, hand-reared birds take longer to achieve this than their more sprightly wild cousins!

It is easiest to get birds on the wing by planting areas of suitable cover from which they are encouraged to fly when the beaters tap them out. It is also possible to put obstacles in their way, such as 'sewelling' but any form of impenetrable barrier such as wire netting is not only inclined to collect groups of birds which flush in a cloud, but exhausts them as they beat against it in an effort to get through (and, if left standing between shooting days, pheasants are easily trapped against it by marauding foxes and dogs).

When sewelling is correctly used it is put up just before the beaters begin the drive and sited in a cleared space on the gunstand side of light ground cover. The space between the sewelling and cover should be at least 10m (11yd). Pheasants moving forward will be suspicious of the sewelling *if it is new to them* and will remain in the cover until tapped out by the beaters.

To ensure a steady rise of birds throughout the drive, the ideal pheasant covert should have patches of flushing cover, such as low shrubs or young naturally regenerated trees, evenly distributed at intervals from the point where the beaters enter. The patches can be about 5m (16.5ft) square, or in the form of strips. From the very start of the drive they should ensure an intermittent rise of the birds as the beaters work their way through. The fewer the patches of cover, the bigger the rise of birds at each flush, the extreme example being where all the birds run forward and rise together at the edge of the wood. Careful beating helps to avoid the problem, even where there is a single flushing point at the end of the drive. But it is better to be certain of a steady stream of birds by having numerous flushing points.

A problem can occur where the area being driven is exceptionally long – more, say, than 200m (220yd). Birds that rise at the beginning of such a drive often come down again before reaching the guns. It is unlikely that they will fly again during a drive, and even if they do they will not fly well. In this case it is advisable to cut or spray out all but a very few patches of cover at the beginning of the drive and concentrate the flushing and holding cover in the last 100m (110yd).

The commonest ground cover in Britain is normally brambles but they do, of course, vary greatly in their types and habit of growth. A light covering 50cm (20in) high which beaters can walk over is ideal, but where the growth is exceptionally vigorous it is only to be expected that they will walk around it. Good Spaniels will solve this problem but they are not always readily available and when they are, not always well disciplined! This poses a very great problem because to trim these areas into manageable sized groups by hand is very expensive and it is not always practicable to use a machine other than a 'pedestrian'-operated one. Some of these of the type known as a 'strimmer' can be very useful but are limited to fairly small areas by their size and consequent speed of use. Brushwood killing sprays can be used but they are expensive and often leave a tangled mass of dead brambles which can be just as much of a problem as live ones. A tractor-mounted brushwood cutter is the ideal answer but hidden tree stumps and fallen branches amongst the dense tangle of brambles can cause damage to the machine.

One method which can be very effective is to tow a heavy log or railway sleeper *sideways* behind a tractor to flatten unwanted cover before the shooting season. If a large hidden tree stump is encountered the worst that can normally happen is a broken towing chain, although I have seen a small tractor rear up like a frightened horse when the log became anchored to a tree stump!

Neglected hazel coppice under large trees poses a different problem. There is usually a completely bare floor with little room above for the

Lonicera nitida growing well in a flushing ride opened up in an old covert

Coppiced conifers such as this spruce can make good flushing cover

A young snowberry flushing point showing how it can be quite accessible for pheasants. It can, however, become too dense in later years and paths will have to be cut

When hurdle making ceases, the result is derelict overgrown hazel

birds to fly up. The answer is to cut out small 'skylights' in the coppice – two or three stools are usually enough – and these skylights should be spaced about 30m (33yd) apart. This system is described in detail in chapter 6. If there is too little natural growth, flushing shrubs such as *Lonicera* and snowberry can be planted in the skylights.

No matter how efficient the flushing cover, some pheasants will inevitably run on to the end. The final flushing point, which must collect these birds, should be most carefully planned (see Fig 6, below). It should not be too small but capable of holding the number of birds which you are expecting without crowding, and it is better to err on the large side to avoid a panicky crowd which will explode in one big flush. The area between the flushing point and the edge of the wood should allow the birds to climb at the required 35° maximum angle towards the trees in front. This 'rising area' will help even the most reluctant fliers to travel high and fast by the time they clear the wood and find themselves in the open.

In a thick tangle of undergrowth, pheasants often penetrate so far that they become trapped and cannot get out, let alone fly. The flushing point should therefore be planted with shrubs which allow the birds to move freely about underneath and excellent species for this purpose are *Lonicera* and snowberry.

Snowberry, with its suckering habit, will spread rapidly but can easily be cut over with a brush cutter and will grow again. The illustration on p. 57 shows how easy it is for birds to move about in it.

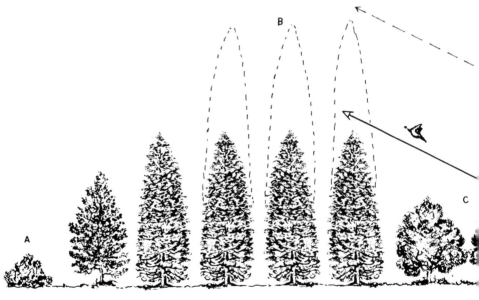

40 METRES

Initial planting should be in groups of six with 1m (3ft) between the plants and 5m (16.5ft) between groups. Evergreen *Lonicera* must be less densely planted: groups of four with 2m (6ft) between plants and 6m (20ft) between groups. Both these planting distances look rather sparse at first but be patient, they will fill up after three or four seasons.

If possible, the shape of a flushing point should be roughly triangular with the point towards the guns so that the moving beaters close up until they are shoulder to shoulder as they approach the point.

Of prime importance is a ride of at least 10m (11yd) wide – and, if there is room, 15m (16.5yd) – round the flushing point. Sewelling can then be run round the outside edge of this ride and out to the edge of

---

Fig 6 Flushing points are a vital part of a pheasant covert: they are designed and sited to allow the birds that have run forward to take wing easily – before they have seen the guns – and gather speed and height before they reach the edge of the wood. In this section of a formal flushing point A represents shelter hedge B – perimeter shelter belt (dotted line shows how the trees will grow) C – rising area of coppice or laurel D – sewelling rides (the sewelling must run along the edge of the nearest rising area) E – flushing shrubs (note how the size of this area must anticipate the growth of the shelter belt area).

Sewelling, which consists of a line of coloured cloth pieces or strips of plastic on a cord stretching down the flushing ride, can be an additional help in getting the birds into the air

Angled rides create this wedge-shaped flushing area in a large woodland. Pheasants are blanked into it from either side and then driven out over guns in the open field

the covert to form two big 'wings' which will funnel the pheasants into the flushing area.

The last third of the flushing point should be screened off by a single row of *Lonicera* – planted 1m (3ft) apart – running across and parallel to the line of beaters. This screen is very important. Observation of pheasants which are being driven out of a wood shows that they reach a critical stage when they either fly or decide that the beaters are too close, bury themselves in cover if it is available, and sit tight. They can be made to rise close to the beaters if they believe they cannot be seen. The screen gives them this facility, an essential feature where a large number of birds may have collected at the end of a covert. It should be kept clipped down to a height of 1m (3ft) so that the beaters can step over it when finishing the drive.

With a very large number of birds it is usually possible for the beaters to stand at the beginning of the flushing point and clap their hands (on no account shout). This should flush a steady stream of pheasants and when the flow begins to die down the beaters can move very slowly forward to the low hedge just described and stand again, clapping hands until they step over the last portion of the flushing point and walk it through, again very slowly. It cannot be over-emphasised how important it is to proceed at a snail's pace at the end of any pheasant drive whether it is in woodland or a game crop. At the least sign of hurrying the birds will double back between the beaters. And, of course, there should be no dogs in the flushing point, however well trained! Another advantage of this system is that if the keeper does not want too many pheasants shot he can quietly draw the beaters back when he has seen enough birds go forward and the rest can be left undisturbed.

THE RISING AREA

This gives the pheasants the all-important gentle gradient after they have taken wing. As already said, it takes a great deal of the 'steam' out of them if they are forced to corkscrew up through tall trees. When this happens they start planing down in all directions as soon as they reach the open, passing low over the guns.

Making provision for this gentle rising gradient is not always easy, because it needs quite a lot of space. Sweet chestnut coppice is the ideal plant: grown on a twelve to sixteen year rotation it is not only of medium height, but it produces durable and valuable fencing stakes. There are, however, only a limited number of areas where it can be grown profitably, mainly in south-east England. Christmas trees would be a good substitute unless it were necessary to wire them against rabbits. Any form of coppice can be planted as an alternative if the soil is unsuitable for chestnut. However, such species as hazel and birch are unlikely to have a market and the area is liable to become neglected, but coppiced ash for firewood is a possibility.

Another suggestion is to plant a one-third crop of trees in rows running away from the flushing point. These should have a very wide gap, about 5–6m (16–20ft) between the rows, leaving a series of corridors through which the birds can fly as they gain height. Larch is a good choice in most places and, with suitable soil, poplars are also successful if planted 6 × 6m (20 × 20ft). If none of these solutions is practicable then common laurel or *Cotoneaster frigidus* would serve the purpose.

In a long, narrow wood of 60–70m (66–77yd) wide it may be difficult to find enough width for a 'set piece' flushing point at the end. A useful compromise is to have groups of *Lonicera* or snowberry on either side of a central ride, forming a long continuous flush.

Where pheasants are reluctant to fly from a large woodland, running them into a projecting game crop before flushing can be very successful

SITING THE NEW COVERT

Anyone with a good eye for shooting country can spot promising sites for pheasant drives. Where the choice exists, it is obviously best to plant on a slightly elevated site. This will enable guns to be placed well below, in the line of flight to other cover. For example, two coverts on opposite sides of a valley can produce high pheasants whichever way they are driven.

Where possible, a site should be chosen which enables the wood to be driven in more than one direction. Advantage can then be taken of a neighbouring crop, or allowance made for a change of wind, although coverts on the boundary will usually have to be driven in towards the centre of the shoot.

The ideal pattern is a compact group of small coverts of 1–2ha (2.5–5 acres) each in a circle around a central, rather larger wood of 4–5ha (10–12 acres). Releasing pheasants in the centre will have the same effect as dropping a stone into the middle of a pool: the birds will ripple out to the smaller coverts from which they can be driven 'home'.

The distance that pheasants will fly varies very much with the type of country. For instance, when flushed from high ground in open rolling downland they will glide for long distances, 700–800m (770–880yd) or more. In country with a lot of cover (small fields with big hedges, woods and spinneys close together) they will tend to come down as soon as possible and it may be difficult to get them to fly more than 150m (165yd). Where the terrain allows it, anything between 200 and 500m (220–550yd) is a reasonable distance between coverts.

Pheasants, however, do not always go the way one wishes them to. For this reason it is wise to carry out a few experiments before committing yourself to the costly and very permanent process of planting a new covert.

Where it is practicable, a trial can be made by planting a temporary game crop in the position you favour and see how it works during the shooting season. It is the flying characteristics that you can establish in this way. It should tell you whether the site is the right distance from a neighbouring covert, the effect of wind, and whether the birds will fan out to give shooting to all the guns. In this respect, it does not

A game spinney designed by the author for the Stechworth Estate at Newmarket owned by the Duke of Sutherland. The guns stand in a deep valley between the spinney and the older woodland beyond. The holding capacity has been increased by planting a crop of Jerusalem artichokes in the foreground

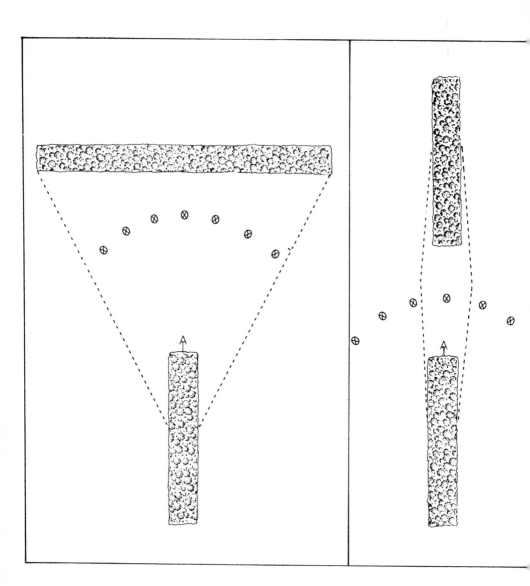

Fig 7 Pheasants driven from a narrow covert or belt towards a wide area of cover will spread evenly over a line of guns

Fig 8 When driven from one narrow covert or belt towards another, pheasants will not stray much outside the area enclosed by the dotted lines. The three centre guns will get all the shooting

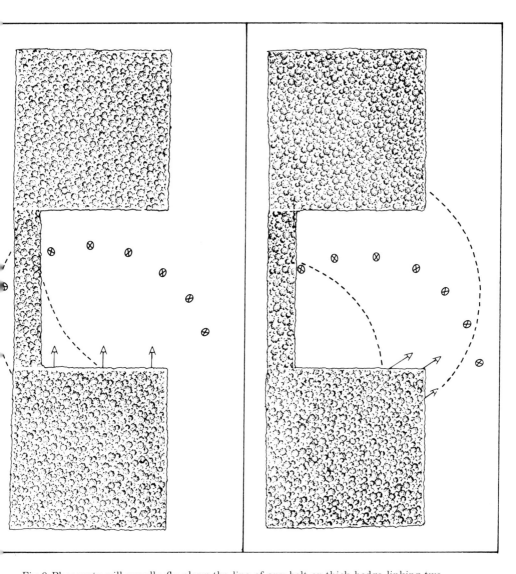

Fig 9 Pheasants will usually fly along the line of any belt or thick hedge linking two coverts. In this example, the two guns on either side of the belt will get all the shooting

Fig 10 The solution to the problem depicted in Fig 9 is to drive the pheasants away from the belt as shown by the arrows. The birds will then spread more evenly over the guns as shown by the dotted lines. A stop must, of course, be placed at the junction of the covert being driven and the belt to prevent birds from running through

matter how narrow the new covert is (it could even be a shelter belt) providing it is aiming at a broad expanse of cover which would, in effect, be 'crossing the T'. The extreme opposite is driving one shelter belt to another in the same line when all the birds will fly over the two guns on either side (see Figs 7 and 8, p. 64).

If you have a home covert in a valley bottom which holds birds well but from which they fly badly, the obvious solution is to plant a new shooting covert on higher ground and link the two with a belt of trees or a double hedge. On a shooting day the pheasants can be blanked out of the home covert into the new shooting covert and then driven back home. However, pheasants like to fly on the same line as they travel on the ground. For this reason they will tend to follow the line of a belt or even a hedge which connects the two coverts. This is known as 'tramlining' and, again, it results in two guns getting all the shooting.

The answer is to site the new covert so that the birds can be driven away from the linking belt or hedge as shown in Figs 9 and 10 on p. 65. For the link itself, two parallel hedges, with a 15m (16.5yd) space between them, are ideal. The hedges must be dense so that the birds can run between them without being seen and *Lonicera* hedges are

A game covert design showing the triangular flushing point with a sweet chestnut coppice rising area in front of it

perfect for this purpose. The space between should be kept clear to make sure that the birds can run through easily.

This system of blanking birds up onto higher ground can be extremely effective on an exposed hillside site. In such a position it might be difficult to hold pheasants which would prefer the more cosy covert down below. In this case the higher site need only be planted in the simplest way and the birds fed there each day to get them used to the link between the two coverts. They could then be easily blanked uphill before the drive started.

To sum up, when siting a new covert, bear in mind the following points:

1. Consider the likely line of flight for the pheasants: is there cover for them to fly to and is it the right distance away?
2. How does the site relate to the covert where you release pheasants: is there a link to encourage the birds to move to the new site?
3. Is the site too close to the boundary of the shoot or to a feature, such as a hedgerow, shelter belt, stream or river, which might lead pheasants over the boundary?
4. Take advantage of any rise in the ground to add height to the birds' flight.
5. Where will you place the guns and will the birds spread evenly over the line?
6. Note how the site relates to the prevailing wind: does it help or hinder the birds in their line of flight to the guns? Can it be driven in more than one direction if the wind is wrong?
7. If the site is very exposed can you be sure that the type of planting you have in mind will provide adequate shelter?
8. A slight dip in the ground of only a couple of metres can make the site more sheltered and attractive.
9. Planting in the lee of an existing shelter belt or hedge can give a valuable initial advantage to tree establishment as well as holding pheasants.
10. Bear in mind how the site relates to disturbance from public footpaths, roads, houses, etc.
11. Consider the soil conditions. For instance, it can be very difficult to establish trees on thin soil over chalk downland.
12. And finally, how will the shape of a new plantation affect the landscape?

4
Coverts, Spinneys, Shelter Belts and Hillside Coverts

This old cottage garden with its existing hedge could be planted quite easily with tree whips to make an excellent game spinney

Fig 11 below shows how the principal features so far described can be put together to form a basic design for a game covert. The sheltering conifers on the outside of the layout are shown as dark trees and the rising area is the triangle in front of the groups of flushing shrubs. The size is purely arbitrary – 330m (363yd) long and 70m (77yd) wide or approximately 5.6ha (14 acres) – and so is the overall shape. The central ride, main tree compartments of mixed species, flushing point and rising areas should always conform as near as possible to the layout shown. This assumes a flat site with the end of the flushing point 70m (77yd) from the perimeter hedge but it could be closer if the site were on a hillside because, in that case, the rising area, which extends for a further 30m (33yd), could be dispensed with. However,

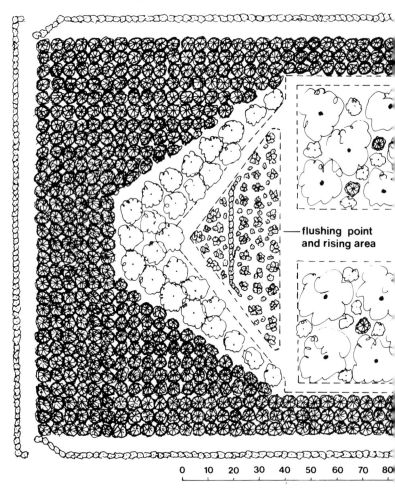

flushing point and rising area

0   10   20   30   40   50   60   70   80

always remember to allow plenty of room for the birds to gain speed before they are clear of the wood and can see the guns. The edge shown is the simplest form but can be modified as discussed in chapter 2.

The practical problems of pegging out a design like this on the ground will mean that it is easier to work with straight or parallel lines for the central area but any irregularities outside this can be filled with conifers as shown in Figs 12–14 on pp. 72–3. It is, of course,

Fig 11 In this standard design for a game covert the dimensions are only a guide. The central stand of hardwoods is headed at the triangular flushing point by the sewelling ride. The whole covert is surrounded by a sheltering conifer belt. Note the conifer wind baffles in the main central ride and the angled entrance ride (see also Figs 12, 13 and 14)

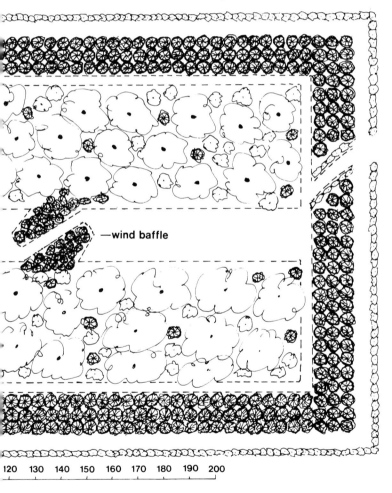

—wind baffle

120 130 140 150 160 170 180 190 200

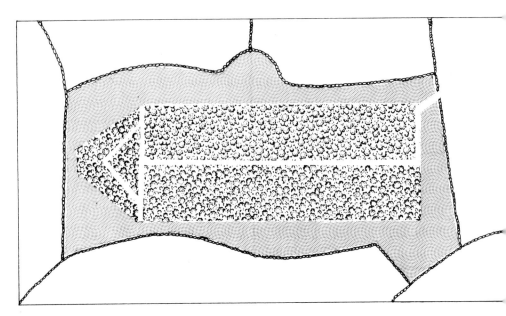

Fig 12 Planting the standard game covert design is simple if the central compartment, flushing point and rising area are laid out as shown and any irregularities in the shape of the site are filled up with conifers. The edge design must always follow the site perimeter line

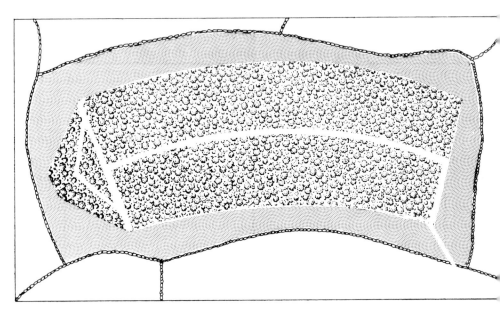

Fig 13 If necessary, the central compartment can be curved but the tree lines can still be kept parallel for ease of planting and management

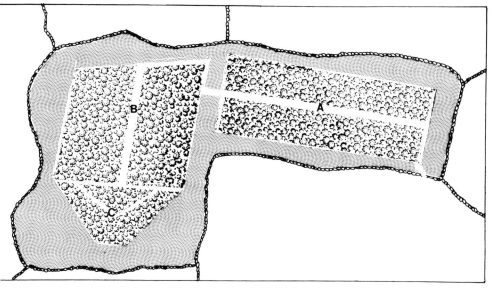

Fig 14 In an 'L' shaped site, the central compartment can be split into two as shown. The pheasants for area A are first blanked into area B. A few stops are left in the area between the two compartments to discourage birds from running back. Meanwhile the rest of the beaters move round to the top of area B in the diagram and drive the pheasants down to the flushing point at C

essential that the edge design you choose follows the outside perimeter of the covert whatever shape it may be.

I first designed this layout in the late 1950s and several have been planted and have proved extremely successful.

BASIC DESIGN FOR A GAME SPINNEY

Fig 15 on p. 75 shows a spinney layout which will meet the requirements of most farms or small estates. Although it is shown here as 50 × 100m (55 × 110yd) or 0.5ha (1.2 acres) it can obviously be increased in length or breadth to suit individual sites. The spinney has four purposes:

(1) *Nesting cover.* The layout provides good nesting cover suitable for both pheasants and partridges, something that can be sadly lacking on a modern arable farm.

(2) *Release point.* The whole centre portion inside the hedge can be wired in to make a release pen for 300–400 reared pheasant poults. This would be much more satisfactory than releasing into a cover crop, from which poults usually stray rather quickly, probably in search of sunshine, warmth and roosting. Since the spinney is also to be used for

73

One of the earliest coverts designed by the author on the Six Mile Bottom shoot near Newmarket, planted in 1957. The extension to the covert to the right in the picture was planted at a later date and guns are placed between the two coverts

nesting and for gathering birds on a shooting day, provision must be made for rolling up the bottom of the netting of the release pen. Gates must also be provided to give access for beaters at both ends.

(3) *Flushing area for an adjoining crop.* The spinney can be expanded for the shooting season by sowing an adjoining crop such as kale, mustard or maize. Birds can be run into the spinney, from which they can be tapped out in a steady stream rather than the big flushes sometimes seen from a crop, particularly maize. If the spinney is sited where four fields meet, this 'expansion' game crop can be planted in seven different positions without using the same ground. The spinney is planned so that it can be driven in either direction.

(4) *Late winter holding cover.* At the end of the shooting season the game crop will be ploughed up and the spinney will continue to provide good holding cover for stock birds for the coming breeding season.

The hedge is *Lonicera nitida*, although ramanas rose is a possible substitute. The outside row of trees should be colourful, of medium height and preferably bearing berries that pheasants will eat. Suitable species are common whitebeam, Swedish whitebeam, mountain ash, common crab apple (or the more ornamental *Malus floribunda*), and standard thorn such as *Crataegus prunifolia*. Next comes a row of fast-growing Leyland cypress for shelter. Possible substitutes are Lawson cypress and western red cedar. Inside the Leyland is a row of larch for roosting. Any of the larches would do but pine could be used, although it would not be so effective. The next row is laurel to complete the draught-proofing of the central area.

On one side of the spinney the outside rows are followed by a feed ride and on the other side by five rows of shrubs and two rows of oak, common oak for preference, but the faster growing red oak could be used. Possible substitutes are sweet chestnut, alder and birch. On alkaline sites beech may have to be used but, if so, plant a row of laurel between them to give some cover in future years.

The central row of shrubs should be tall berry-bearing varieties such as *Cotoneaster frigidus* or *C. cornubia*. Plant the remaining four rows with a mixture; the following species are all suitable to choose from: hawthorn, guelder rose, wayfarer bush, and any of the reasonably low-growing *Cotoneasters* such as *distichus, horizontalis* or *simonsii*.

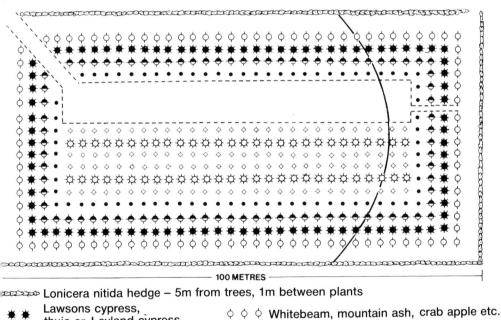

|—— 100 METRES ——|

〰〰〰 Lonicera nitida hedge – 5m from trees, 1m between plants

✳ ✳ Lawsons cypress, thuja or Leyland cypress

◆ ◆ Larch

✿ ✿ Oak

◇ ◇ ◇ Whitebeam, mountain ash, crab apple etc.

• • • Laurel

◇ ◇ ◇ Various shrubs (see text)

All trees and shrubs [except lonicera] to be planted 2.5m × 2.5m

Fig 15 A Basic Design for a Game Spinney

75

The hedge of *Lonicera* should be planted as a single row at 1m (3ft) spacing. All the remaining plants should be 2.5m (8ft) apart with 2.5m (8ft) between the rows. This applies to shrubs as well as trees.

As with the game covert layout, any irregularities in the shape of the site can be filled in with conifers or medium height hardwoods but the edge design must follow right around the line of the perimeter.

The number of plants required for a spinney of the size shown is as follows:

Lonicera nitida (or ramanas rose) 300	oak 60
outside row of trees 100	laurel 75
Leyland cypress 92	tall *Cotoneaster* 30
larch 86	remaining shrubs 120

I have not included a formal flushing point and rising area. This is because the whole of the central compartment is, in effect, a flushing area since the light canopy of trees will allow birds to rise easily from the shrub cover. All that is necessary on a shooting day is to run sewelling round the end of the central compartment nearest the guns and out to the boundary hedges. The sewelling should not be put straight across the spinney but follow a curved line as shown in the diagram. An area 10m (11yd) wide should be kept mown short along the line of the sewelling where this passes through the central compartment and this will eventually become an established flushing ride as the spinney matures. Some shrubs may eventually have to be removed to achieve this but not for several years.

THE 'INSTANT' GAME SPINNEY

Many shoots use annual game crops on the same sites each year because they know they make good pheasant drives. There are two obvious disadvantages to this. First, the ground can get 'sick', particularly with continuous planting of one species, such as kale. Secondly, there is the problem of annual cultivation. The modern farm demands large fields, and drilling small patches of game crops can be very time-consuming and expensive to establish as well as being difficult to fit into the hard-pressed work pattern of the farm. All too often this leads to late planting and insufficient cultivation resulting in a poor crop full of weeds.

As a solution, the tendency has been to take the game crop area out of the farm and plant it up as a permanent spinney. In the long term this is the best answer, but it does produce short-term problems. The young trees must be protected from rabbits and hares (and deer if present), and the only suitable method with small transplants – 60cm

A recently planted instant spinney in an awkward-shaped corner of a field

(2ft) or less in height – is to fence the whole area with rabbit netting. This can account for more than 50 per cent of the total cost of a small plantation. It also discourages pheasants from using it because they much prefer access on foot to flying in and out. Young chicks, hatched in attractive nesting cover, usually find it impossible to get out into the neighbouring fields because grasses and weeds will choke up the meshes of the rabbit netting. (Incidentally, trials have shown that pheasant chicks up to nine days old pass through 3cm (1¼in) mesh netting if the mesh is kept open.)

Plantations on arable sites invariably become covered with a dense mass of grass weeds as opposed to the shrubby species of old woodland sites. This rank growth is unattractive to pheasants, except during the nesting season, and the new planting will be little used in wintertime until the trees have begun to suppress the grass, a process which can take several years. In many cases, therefore, the landowner finds that he has to continue planting a game crop alongside the new spinney for some years until the wire netting has been removed and the trees have suppressed some of the weed growth.

Some years ago, Sir Kynaston Studd Bt of the Manor Farm, Rockbourne, who had experienced all these problems, suggested that there might be a case for planting bigger trees at wider spacing with protective sleeves to eliminate the need for rabbit netting, which is not only very expensive but extremely difficult to keep secure. At this time the use of trees 1.5m (5ft) high ('whips' or 'half standards') was becoming popular and they were therefore fairly readily available. Only hardwoods are practicable since large conifers are very difficult to transplant successfully.

Baron Knigge in one of the instant spinneys on his estate in West Germany. The artichokes are rather too vigorous! *Pinus mugo* planted experimentally between the hardwoods was not successful

The reason for using whips is that they are tall enough to be fitted with protective sleeves and do not require weeding. Small transplants, 40cm (16in) high, will always do better in the long run but until now it has been expensive to protect them from pests and weeds. The development of the plastic 'tree shelter' (see photograph on p.111) has now made it possible to overcome this difficulty. Trees protected in this way grow rapidly, although this in itself may cause problems because they may be soft and easily blown over. Time will tell.

At Rockbourne, we planted a spinney using whips but soon found that the rank growth of grass weeds and the lack of shelter due to wide tree spacing made it unattractive to pheasants. We then put in a few conifers, which promptly got eaten by rabbits, then wired the whole area and virtually started again. In other words, it was for a time an unholy mess, although it is now, after twelve years, a very useful little spinney.

It was obvious, however, that the key to the problem was to eliminate the grass weeds in favour of something more attractive, and it was then that I hit on the idea of Jerusalem artichokes and the 'instant spinney' was born – instant because it can provide shooting from the first season it is planted. It is, in effect, a perennial game crop with a spinney growing through it.

By using hardwood whips with sleeves and hedges of *Lonicera*, which is rarely damaged by rabbits or hares, the need for rabbit netting, or any fencing where there is no farm livestock, is eliminated. The space between the tree lines is planted with four rows of Jerusalem artichokes to provide ground cover, suppress weeds and shelter the growing trees. A refinement to this is to substitute five rows of canary grass (*Phalaris tuberosa*) for the artichokes between the two outside tree lines. This will warm up the artichokes which can be draughty in late winter.

A detailed cross-section of the design is shown in Fig 16 on pp. 80–1 and it is important to understand the thinking behind it. First and foremost is the question of the edge because of its importance to the game and the farm. The double hedges are 5m (16.5ft) apart and continue right round the spinney thus ensuring that there is always shelter from wind whichever quarter it may blow from. The plants are 1m (3ft) apart in the rows. As the species used is *Lonicera*, these hedges require virtually no maintenance.

The double hedge of *Lonicera nitida* surrounding an instant spinney provides excellent ground level shelter from wind

The first row of trees is 3m (10ft) from the inside hedge and it is important to choose the right species which must be of medium height. The most suitable species are those already suggested for the outside row of the basic game spinney (see Fig 15, p. 75). This outside row of trees continues right round the spinney. The next row is 6m (20ft) further in and the larger species can now be used. Those which produce useful winter food for the birds, such as oak, sweet chestnut, alder and birch, are to be preferred. If beech has to be used on an alkaline site then some groups of laurel should be planted with them, the plants being protected by wire netting or sleeves. All the large trees are spaced 3m (10ft) apart in rows 6m (20ft) apart, and there is no tall tree less than 14m (46ft) from the farm headland which virtually removes any possibility of their competing with the farm crops.

The layout shown in Fig 16 is 68m (75yd) wide but this can of course be decreased if required by, for instance, leaving out the central ride and one row of trees which would reduce it to 56m (62yd), but it would be unwise to bring it down any further. The width, however, should not be excessive otherwise it will need too many beaters to drive it on a shooting day. The length can be anything that is convenient but should not be less than 100m (110yd).

Fig 16 The 'Instant' Game Spinney
Game crops, when correctly sited and suited to the local soil conditions, will greatly improve the pheasant holding capacity of a shoot. They can be 'stop-gap' coverts while the long term forestry policy is developing, or used as extra cover planned in conjunction with woodlands. They may, however cause headaches to the farm manager. It is often better in the long run to plant up a permanent spinney, using game crops to shelter the young trees in the early years and provide almost 'instant' shooting cover. In this section through the author's planting plan for an 'instant' spinney, the edge is designed with particular attention to any effect it might have on the farm headland. Ground cover for pheasants is provided by Jerusalem artichokes or canary grass (or a combination of both) planted between the tree lines

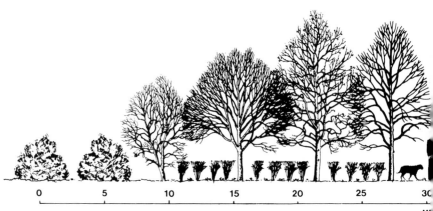

| 0 | 5 | 10 | 15 | 20 | 25 | 3C |

ME

If the site is an irregular shape the two hedges should follow the outside edge and extra trees can be used to fill in any spaces that occur as a result. You may be lucky enough to have no problems with rabbits or hares, in which case you can infill between the trees in their rows with shrubs such as those I have suggested for the basic spinney.

The trees and hedges in the spinney require no management after planting except to replace any failures. A straw mulch (see chapter 2) should be applied to the *Lonicera* and can be used successfully on the trees as well, despite the commonly held view that it encourages vole damage.

The artichokes do require occasional attention. After two or three years they tend to get weedy and the temptation is to cultivate the rows after the shooting season. You should avoid this *at all costs*, because it is very important to keep the rows intact. If they are chopped up the plants will spread and become very dense making it difficult for birds or beaters to get through them. The answer is to weed them chemically using a non-residual spray before the plants show above the ground. This is particularly effective in dealing with grass weeds which can completely suppress artichokes. Canary grass should need no management but it does not usually provide any cover until its second growing season. In the first year of planting it can be oversown with mustard as a temporary measure, but do not put the mustard in until the canary grass is well established: mid-July is quite early enough. Leave the space between the hedges to grass over naturally as nesting cover.

As with the basic spinney design, a formal flushing point and rising area is unnecessary because the combination of a very open tree canopy, with the artichokes and canary grass as ground cover, make for an ideal combination to allow pheasants to rise without hindrance. A flushing ride for sewelling should be cut through the ground cover at

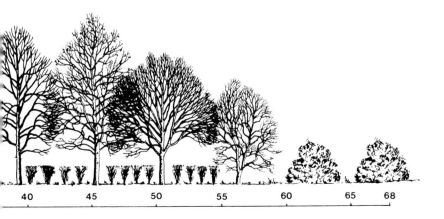

| 40 | 45 | 50 | 55 | 60 | 65 | 68 |

the gunstand end, again following a mowed line as in the basic spinney.

For anyone under the age of fifty I would recommend the standard spinney layout, which in the long term will be a better permanent answer, but for those who are, shall we say, getting a little short of time, I would suggest the instant spinney.

GAME AND FARM SHELTER BELT

Many shelter belts established in the early part of the century have deteriorated to such an extent that they are now virtually useless or at best only partly effective. This appears to be particularly true on arable land where marginal hedges have been grubbed up and the plough taken right up to the trees. In some instances on stock farms, animals have been allowed to graze into belts (as well as woods) making them bare and open at ground level. Where this occurs in a narrow belt you get a venturi effect and the wind, forcing its way through the stems of the trees, can actually increase its speed for a short distance before and after it has passed through the belt.

(*left*) Even with a hedge this beech belt is of no benefit to game in winter and provides poor nesting cover in the summer

(*right*) The open stems of this Scots pine belt produce a venturi effect which actually increases the ground level wind speed both before and after the wind passes through. It is essential to have a medium height edge species to close this gap

A combination of dense shade from the beech canopy and free access for farm animals makes this spinney valueless for game. If fenced and planted with a common privet perimeter hedge it would be much improved

For a belt to be efficient as a windbreak it must have shelter at all levels of height. Rows of naked trees like so many telegraph poles are ineffective. Animals and birds lose a great deal of body heat when exposed to cold winds without shelter. (American game management technicians who planted shelter belts for game found that heat losses in some Midwest farmsteads were so reduced by the windbreaks that fuel bills for the animals kept indoors and for the household fell by as much as 30 per cent.)

The function of a shelter belt is not to stop the wind since this would only produce a violent downdraught on the lee side and flatten the crops there. The aim should be to filter the wind and slow it down. A solid barrier has to be very wide, 100m (110yd) or more, so that the turbulence is absorbed by the belt itself. This sort of width would not be acceptable on a valuable arable farm. The best layout is pyramid in shape so that the wind is led up into the tree canopy which is fairly thin and which erodes the wind speed rather than trying to stop it. The pyramid form also keeps the tree shade as far back from the farm headland as possible.

A thin belt of two rows of trees and a straggling hedge will reduce the wind speed by a constant amount of about 20 per cent for a distance

(*above*) An excellent young shelter belt on a Hampshire estate. Scots pine in the centre with sweet chestnut coppice alongside and a well trimmed hawthorn hedge

(*right*) The young shelter belt in close up showing how the Scots pine are well back from the farm headland, the chestnut occupying the intervening space

of fifteen times the tree height. A well-designed belt, on the other hand, will reduce it by 80 per cent at first, dropping steadily to 20 per cent at the same distance.

A shelter belt provides an enormous proportion of edge to area when compared to a square or rectangular wood. Partly for this reason, country where belts are common, such as the Brecklands of East Anglia, is highly productive for wild pheasants and partridges. The edge design is vitally important for both game and farm for the reasons previously stated, as well as for the additional low shelter that it provides.

Most shelter belts planted today are similar in layout to those established forty or fifty years ago. In those days large farm staffs were available in the winter months for the traditional work of 'hedging and ditching' and the drastic reduction of this labour force has contributed to the neglect of the old belts. As in woodland, one must plant today for efficient and rapid mechanical management, and these requirements are met by the shelter belt which I designed many years ago and which is shown in cross-section in Fig 17 on pp. 86–7. It can be conveniently

divided into four sections: hedge, perimeter zone, coppice and central compartment.

The hedge and perimeter zone are repeated from the woodland layout and serve the same function. The perimeter zone provides the principal source of nesting cover, particularly for partridges, which prefer not to nest under trees. This space can be used to grow three rows of Christmas trees each side in the early stages. For every 100m (110yd) of belt, 300 Christmas trees can be planted at 1×1m (3×3ft) spacing. This Christmas tree crop can make a very significant contribution to the cost of fencing which is extremely high for the area enclosed. For instance, 400m (440yd) of belt 25m (27.5yd) wide occupies 1ha (2.47 acres) and requires 850m (935yd) of fencing. The same length of fencing will enclose a wood 212m (233yd) square, which amounts to 4.5ha (11 acres). After the Christmas trees have been removed, the space on one side could be used as a farm track if the width were slightly increased when planting, but care should be taken to choose the shaded or windy side, leaving the most sun and shelter for the game.

As the trees in the centre grow to maturity their lower branches will die off and when this happens the hedge alone will not provide enough shelter to avoid the venturi effect. It could, of course, be allowed to grow tall if it were thorn but this could make it thin at the bottom and the wind would whistle through at ground level – just where it is not wanted. This problem can only be solved by planting a medium-height evergreen shrub inside the perimeter zone and laurel is the obvious

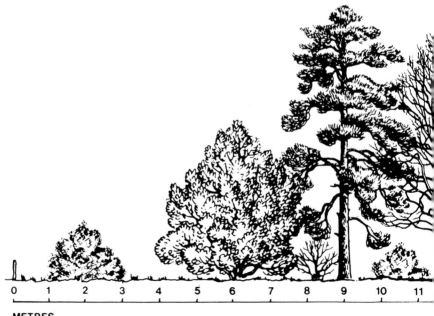

0   1   2   3   4   5   6   7   8   9   10   11

METRES

choice. It is necessary to have this medium height species on *both* sides of the belt to keep the shade line back from the farm but evergreen laurel need only be *one* side to give wind protection, preferably the windward side. A different deciduous shrub could be used for the other side – perhaps one of the taller *Cotoneasters* such as *frigidus* or *cornubia* which are particularly good. If the soil were suitable an alternative would be sweet chestnut coppiced to provide a regular crop of good-quality fence posts (see photograph on p. 84). Whatever species is used in these rows, the spacing between the plants should be 3m (10ft). The hedge should be *Lonicera* at 1m (3ft) but in very exposed or high-altitude sites, a tree hedge such as Sitka spruce would be preferred, *providing* it is accessible for a tractor-mounted cutter to top it occasionally. The pea tree could also be considered as a hedge in exposed conditions.

The space between the rows of trees should be 3m (10ft), which can be left to facilitate mechanical weeding or planted up with groups of

---

Fig 17 A Basic Design for a Game and Farm Shelter Belt
Shelter belts can be highly productive for both wild pheasants and partridges: it provides a high proportion of edge to area when compared to a conventional wood. A badly designed belt, however, can create a downdraught on the lee side and flatten the crops there. A well planned belt filters the wind and slows it down, as opposed to acting like a brick wall. All planting should be designed for efficient and rapid mechanical management and have a dual function serving both the farm and the game. Note the careful edge layout of hedge and laurel to reduce the effect of shade on the farm headland and lead the wind into the tree canopy

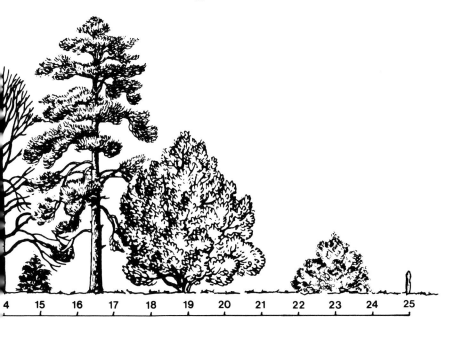

| 4 | 15 | 16 | 17 | 18 | 19 | 20 | 21 | 22 | 23 | 24 | 25 |

cover shrubs such as snowberry, *Lonicera* or, on chalkland sites, common privet. The spacing between the trees in their rows should be 2m (6ft).

With the two marginal strips established – hedge, perimeter zone and coppice or shrubs – the central compartment can be any width convenient to the site, although an overall width of 25m (27.5yd) for the whole belt must be considered the minimum. The choice of tree species for the centre is not as important as their management. Whatever species is chosen, it is necessary to thin the trees when they are about 8–10m (26–33ft) high in order to break the canopy. This will not only produce the right filter effect for reducing the wind speed, but sunlight will reach the ground, allowing the growth of ground cover. Of course, seed-bearing hardwoods such as oak, chestnut or beech are advantageous and provide a pleasing diversion from the regimentation of pure conifers, but softwoods make better shelter than hardwoods and

Fig 18 An Alternative Design for a Game and Farm Shelter Belt
Shelter belts are expensive to plant if they have to be fenced against rabbits and hares. Shown here is a design for an unfenced shelter belt using individually protected trees and shrubs and unprotected *Lonicera nitida* hedges. Good ground cover is provided initially by rows of canary grass between the tree and shrub lines. If the belt can be made 3m wider the laurel can be planted down the centre between the rows of alder and another row of berried shrubs or small trees put on the right hand side (where the laurel is shown in the diagram). This would have the advantage of making the laurel less visible since it is not a very attractive plant

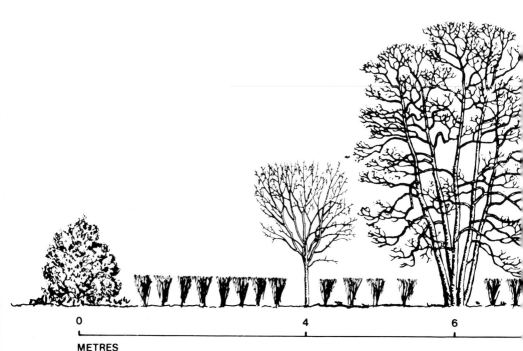

0   4   6

METRES

are the most likely choice, particularly on exposed sites. There are some very attractive belts in Norfolk where the species is basically larch and Scots pine but copper beech has been planted every 50m (55yd) or so and makes a splendid contrast in colour and texture.

The layout proposed here is also valuable when the time comes for the trees to be felled, either as saleable timber or through eventual deterioration with age. Replanting the central area will then be much easier, with the old hedge and coppice still providing good shelter for the young trees. Throughout its whole existence it can be easily managed and will provide good nesting and winter cover for both partridges and pheasants.

THE UNFENCED GAME SHELTER BELT

After the introduction of the 'instant spinney' I was asked if the same principles could be used for shelter belts which were needed across an area of newly cultivated fenland on an estate in Norfolk. As this type of land is so enormously valuable, it was necessary to keep the width of the belt down to a minimum. In a narrow belt, artichokes were unlikely to provide sufficient shelter and so I suggested canary grass alone. My original layout was 20m (22yd) wide, but I have now reduced this to 15m (16.5yd). The main tree species is alder (common, grey or Italian) in two rows which can be coppiced as shown in Fig 18 below.

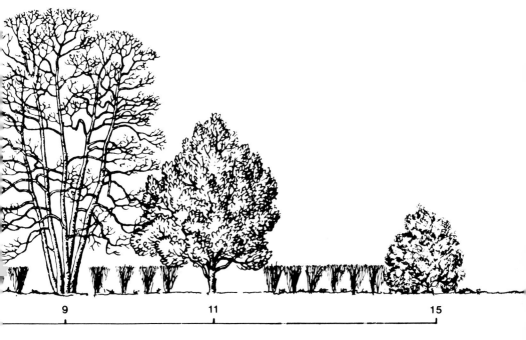

9   11   15

On one side of the alder is laurel and on the other a berry-bearing shrub or small thorn tree such as *Crataegus prunifolia* or a crab, *Malus floribunda*. The laurel and any other shrub used need wire-netting sleeves for protection.

If the belt can be made 3m (10ft) wider, the laurel can be planted down the centre between the rows of alder, and another row of berried shrubs or small trees put on the right-hand side (where the laurel is shown in Fig 18). This has the advantage of making the laurel less visible since it is not a very attractive plant.

Although this type of belt is not so effective for shelter as the first one described, it takes up much less room, is excellent for game and costs less to plant than the fencing alone for a traditional type of planting.

HILLSIDE COVERTS

Many woods are situated on exposed hillsides and these steep sites pose different game-management problems from those encountered on relatively level ground. For instance, a perimeter hedge and belt may only provide effective shelter for a small marginal fringe at the bottom of the wood, the remaining area being open to wind blowing over the top of the belt. Contour shelter belts, as shown in Fig 19 are the best answer to this problem.

A

Fig 19 Hillside coverts – particularly if they are not on the sunny south facing side – can become cold and draughty at certain stages of development. Baffles against the wind can be provided by planting lines or groups of conifers at A, B and C in the diagram. Experience will show whether it is best to drive the birds over guns stationed in the valley below – assuming they can be flushed sufficiently far back – or whether the birds fly more readily along the sides of the valley, the main guns being placed in intersecting rides. Sometimes pheasants can be successfully driven *uphill*, curling back over the guns in the valley below

91

On sloping sites the perimeter shelter belt is more important than a wall or hedge on the extreme edge. *Thuja* is here giving wind protection to the more open larch behind. Further rows of evergreens as shown in Fig 19 (see pages 90–1) would give continuity of shelter

Since most steep sites tend to be exposed, the choice of species is likely to be limited. It is very important, therefore, to decide on the amount of emphasis to be placed on the game content at the earliest stage of planning. The wish to avoid uneconomic early thinnings and the risk of windblow, particularly on sites which may be remote and expensive for extraction, makes wide plant spacing an attractive proposition. This will certainly help to admit more sunlight in the early life of the wood, but as the main canopy grows this advantage will eventually be lost. Using the system of contour shelter belts, it would be advisable to plant the intervening spaces as 'game strips' as shown in Fig 15. These need not be entirely uneconomic. Groups of pine and larch, for instance, could alternate with similar groups of hardwoods, such as oak, ash and rowan, so that half the area of each strip would be sealed off from the wind. The number of 'game strips' included would have to depend on the economic balance between sport and forestry in each case. Even so, the tree growth on a north-facing wood would surely benefit from a general distribution of warmth in this way.

Mechanical maintenance of rides is often not practicable since, apart from the steepness, hillsides frequently have broken ground and outcrops of rock. However, the soil is often rather poor and this, coupled with the exposed aspect, will usually inhibit too much growth in the rides which should always be on a north/south axis where this is possible, since this will admit the most sun.

There is no point in planting hedges where they cannot be maintained, and for this reason one may sometimes be left with only one hedge along the bottom. However, the stone walls found in many upland areas can be invaluable substitutes for hedges.

The flushing points in these steep-sided coverts need careful planning. In a fairly small wood on the Sussex Downs I have seen wonderful pheasants shown by driving them uphill and out of the top, to break back over guns along the floor of the valley. This works particularly well if the birds can fly across to another covert but in larger woods it is usually not practicable, and the birds must normally be driven downhill to a more conventional flushing point. The slope, if over 25°, eliminates the necessity for a rising area. If the wood does not run to the bottom of the slope, leaving plenty of room to place a line of guns well below it, there is no need to have the flushing point inside. In this instance, a strip about 10m (11yd) wide should be planted up with flushing shrubs outside the bottom row of trees. The disadvantage of this system is that if the birds run to the edge and see the guns before they flush, a number may break back. To discourage this, a dense hedge, such as *Lonicera*, should be planted all along the extreme edge at very close spacing (0.5m or 20in) to prevent the birds from pushing through it. A stone wall would be even better.

If the wood runs to the bottom of the slope then the pheasants must be flushed before they run to the end and the answer here is to leave one of the strips between the contour belts unplanted and on a shooting day run a line of sewelling along the lower side of this space to flush the birds.

This type of site is often dismissed out of hand as impracticable for shooting, but this is not so if the problems are carefully thought out before planting. They will certainly not hold many pheasants, however, if sheep are allowed to roam about in them at will. Sheep are little better than goats (the cause of many of the world's deserts) and will leave a bare and inhospitable wood behind them.

5

Large Woodlands and Tree Factories

Large woodlands, in this context, are those in excess of 5ha (12 acres). Incorporating the necessary features to provide good breeding and holding conditions for game in more extensive areas is not very difficult, but it is quite a challenging task to plan the shooting, especially with the object of showing reasonably high birds. There are three problems:

1. If the areas is flat, the birds will usually fly at tree-top height, often making for indifferent shooting.
2. It can be difficult to get pheasants to fly out of a big wood and over the guns standing in the open.
3. Unless the rides and flushing points are carefully sited and the quantity and position of the ground cover managed, all day can be spent in moving the birds without getting them to fly over the guns. The worst thing that can happen is when the birds run forward and finally flush much too close to the guns (see photograph on p. 53).

Solving the problem of showing high, fast birds is, to some extent, a matter of luck and depends on the lie of the land. If your woods are in undulating country then it is obviously easier to choose low places for the guns rather than try to make the birds fly higher. When planning flushing points and gunstands, therefore, advantage should be taken of every hill and valley to increase the distance between the birds and the guns (see also chapter 3). For instance, where there is a small valley within the wood at one end, it is often possible to blank the whole wood up into an area beyond and bring the birds back over the guns standing in the valley. Indeed, valleys are priceless and should only be planted with trees after very careful assessment of the likely effect on the shooting.

A nearby covert or crop which is attractive to pheasants may make it possible to drive them out of a large wood and any projections should be planned to take advantage of this. If a crop such as sugar beet or kale runs right up to a wood, a successful drive can sometimes be made by lining the guns and beaters along the edge and driving away from it

Tree line kept back from a small river. The space could well be doubled with very little loss to a big forest

so that the birds curl back over the beaters to the guns. When doing this, it is best for the guns to follow the beaters out until they are about 30m (33yd) or so from the wood, and then stand in full view of the birds as they fly back. This can be particularly effective if there is a strong wind blowing towards the wood.

The beating of large compartments divided by narrow winding rides frequently allows pheasants to 'leak out' at the sides during the drive. Dividing rides should, therefore, be as wide as possible to enable beaters and guns to contain the birds within the drive more easily. Preferably, these rides should also converge so that the birds are concentrated into a good flushing point where the beaters are much closer together. New rides can be made as described in chapter 2.

When planning the replanting of a large woodland area, the siting of the compartments and the choice of species can have a critical effect on the shooting. For instance, as a long-term plan, small manageable compartments for shooting can be planted with a good mixture of

Fig 20 To show sporting pheasants to the guns in a large woodland, advantage must be taken of any favourable contours to increase the distance between birds and guns. In the top example the birds are rising close to the guns and in line with the beater, a classic opportunity for a dangerous shot. In the lower example the gun-ride has been opened up and a flushing ride cut at the top of the slope (see also Fig 21 pages 98–9). Sewelling must be run along the side of this ride nearest the guns

species and surrounded by larger compartments of pure dense-canopied conifers. In this way a 30ha (74 acre) wood could be split into five 2ha (5 acre) pheasant drives separated by conifer blocks from which any birds could easily be blanked before a drive.

There is no doubt that the big woodland provides the most difficult problems when considered from the point of view of game management. I have come across several unfortunate cases where the forestry had been let on a long lease and the sporting right retained. In one instance I had to advise a syndicate not to renew their lease of the shooting because the coverts would be unshootable within five years. Nothing had been written into the original forestry lease to protect the sporting interest and the whole area is now 275ha (680 acres) of ugly jungle divided into 25ha (62 acre) compartments, which would need an army of beaters to drive them, and nowhere to flush the birds or stand the guns. This wood is only twenty-five miles from London and has ruined a shoot with a potential rental value of £10,000 per annum. One wonders what the forestry department would say if this loss was put as a fixed charge against them!

It is obviously impossible to lay down hard and fast rules because no two large woodlands are alike. In flat country it is virtually impossible to show high pheasants inside the woodland. The only way to encourage the pheasants to rise above tree-top height would be to let them see the guns well before they reached them. With the birds flying

A   D

at, perhaps, 30mph (48kph) they need to spot the guns a long way ahead in order to climb appreciably higher before passing over them and the rides for the guns to stand in would therefore need to be 100m (110yd) or more in width. To accommodate eight guns comfortably this would require an area of about 4ha (10 acres) to be cleared; hardly likely to be acceptable in a commercial forest. The best solution is to have game crops or spinneys well away from the main wood, feed the birds out into these and then drive them back across the guns standing in open ground.

In obvious contrast, flushing birds from high ground across guns standing in valleys can make very attractive shooting. Nevertheless, there is still the problem of the pheasants running on to the guns unless flushing points are properly sited and maintained. In large woods, this is usually best accomplished by cutting flushing rides parallel to the gunstand rides with good shrub cover along the edge furthest away from the guns. Sewelling can then be used to rise the

Fig 21 Large Woodlands
In mature woodland, flushing rides or clearings, can often be made without removing excessive numbers of trees. All shrubs, coppice and poor trees should be cleared from the area between A and B leaving room for a tractor and scrub cutter to keep the ground clear. The trees between B and C should be thinned to encourage the growth of flushing cover. The sewelling line is set at D, and should be clearly visible to the birds at least 15m away

B   C

birds on a shooting day. Fig 20 on pp. 96–7 shows how such a flushing ride should be sited.

In mature hardwoods the flushing point would be more in a clearing than a ride because it would only be necessary to remove a few trees to open the canopy for rising birds. The important feature would be to remove all the ground cover in front of the flushing cover so that the sewelling would be clearly visible to them at least 15m (16.5yd) away (see Fig 21 on pp. 98–9). This is not a particularly difficult task and, since it does not usually require the removal of any good timber trees, should be quite possible for a shoot manager to carry out even if he only rents the sporting rights.

The new owner or tenant of a large area of woodland can be faced with a daunting task during his first shooting season. First, if he is going to release hand-reared pheasants, he must decide how many to release, and where to site the release pen. If he has a 20ha (50 acre) wood then 400 pheasants might seem a reasonable quantity. But it is only 20 birds per hectare (8 per acre) and, if the ground cover is fairly dense and evenly spread throughout the wood, a recovery rate of 10–15 per cent during the shooting season might be the best that could be expected. The logical position for the release pen might seem to be the centre of the wood but the necessary physical requirements may not be there and, in addition, access for feeding and watering might be a problem. The position of the shoot boundary in relation to the wood will also affect the choice of release pen site.

The number of pheasants released will obviously be dictated largely by economics but with a 20ha (50 acre) wood 750 is probably the minimum required to provide a fair return for an eight-gun team. It is impossible to put every bird in the wood over the guns on a shooting day, although with return drives the number might be close to the total population of the wood. There is always a significant proportion of pheasants who manage to avoid being flushed and, as the shooting season progresses, this proportion increases. This is because although the number of birds decreases, the amount of cover (ie places where pheasants can hide) remains the same, and a higher proportion of birds at each shoot are those that have learned to survive! Obviously, the more birds that are released then the more there are 'at risk' on a shooting day and thus the recovery rate is very much a function of density, providing the pre-shoot management is competent.

When choosing the release pen site the requirements of the pheasants should take priority over the convenience of the game-keeper. A useful rule-of-thumb guide is that the site should be roughly divided into three proportions: one-third open sunny ground with short grass, one-third light ground cover such as brambles, and one-third containing low roosting such as young conifers or large shrubs. The roosting can be in one large group if necessary but the ground cover should be in small, evenly distributed patches interspersed with sunny tracks so that the pheasant poults always have cover nearby if threatened for instance by hawks or other pheasants intent on pecking their feathers out. A good distribution of winding, sunny tracks allows the food to be spread over as wide an area as possible to avoid crowding. Pheasants fed in a quarrelling heap on a patch of mud never prosper.

Success during the shooting season will largely depend on two factors: the feeding routine and the physical characteristics of the wood itself. Correct feeding will greatly help to concentrate the pheasants where they are wanted rather than having them spread all over the wood. However, when the first shot is fired on a shooting day every bird will be alerted and the more shots there are the more alert they will be. What most of them will do is go into cover and management should aim to concentrate the best cover in the areas where the birds are needed. This is not an easy task and is sometimes impossibly costly in a large woodland area. Supposing the 20ha (50 acre) wood could be divided up into five drives on a shooting day, then the best cover should be left at the flushing end of each drive and form an area of about 1–1.5ha (2.5–4 acres).

If a woodland has little ground cover but the possibility of growing more if the tree canopy is opened, then the answer is obvious: thin those areas where cover is needed and leave the rest as it is. It is surprising how often this is possible, but equally often it is badly carried out because the shoot manager has not thought the problem through and works sporadically and to no overall plan. This usually results in some areas with too much cover and others with none.

Before undertaking any physical alterations to the wood it is therefore essential first to estimate as accurately as possible what the effect of the work is going to be and how best to make use of this effect.

If you can be patient, make a few experimental cuttings on a small scale and observe the result after one or, even better, two growing seasons. In a rich old hardwood stand comparatively little work may be needed because of the vigorous regeneration of ground cover under a recently thinned tree canopy and a few skylights at each flushing area may suffice. If there is a high proportion of replanted ground less than twenty years old then it will probably not be possible to make any great alterations.

Big woodland areas are very frustrating to the game manager. In a perfect world there would be a law against any wood that was larger than 3ha (7 acres) and closer than 200m (220yd) to the next one!

THE TREE FACTORY

The much-debated pros and cons of the monocultural conifer forest in Great Britain fall outside the scope of this book, but the game and wildlife aspects of the large commercial conifer forest are relevant to our discussion.

Some years ago, in co-operation with the Forestry Commission, I carried out a broad survey of a number of different forests in Scotland and the north of England. More recently, I took part in a very interesting exercise in the Commission's Thetford Forest, which is unique in being the only pure conifer forest that I know which produces a significant crop of wild pheasants. It is, of course, situated in the centre of what used to be the best wild game country in England, and its successful production of game is surely due to the predominance of native Scots pines, which allow a reasonable growth of good ground cover, and to the excellent pattern of extraction rides which provide a fair proportion of edge.

The whole 20,000ha (50,000 acre) area was planted between the years 1925 and 1940 and was one of the earliest major plantings carried out by the Forestry Commission (formed in 1919). Virtually the entire forest will be cropped and replanted during the next twenty years, and Roderick Hewitt, the Conservator, decided to consult representatives of game, wildlife and landscape interests and invite them to make suggestions for any modifications that might be introduced during this process, bearing in mind that Thetford is a commercial forest and the principal object is to produce sound timber at the most economic price. Any suggestions to improve the game crop which would reduce the timber crop as a consequence would therefore require a compensatory increase in the sporting rents to tenant sportsmen.

A 1,000ha (2,500 acre) section of the forest, regarded as being typical of the whole area was used as a study area. After careful survey and assessment, I came to the conclusion that there was no way in which the game crop and shooting facility could be significantly improved without making a fairly large dent in the tree crop. For instance, adding a 10m (11yd) wide habitat strip along one side of all the north/south rides would alone take 5.5 per cent of the timber crop area. The small increase in the wild pheasant production would certainly not have justified an inevitable swingeing increase in the rent. The same increase in pheasants could be achieved with much greater

(*above left*) A dense tree canopy means poor ground cover

(*below left*) Where practical, thinning is the right answer and ground cover will prosper in the resulting sunshine. The quality of the timber will also improve

A straightforward commercial forest plantation with no concessions to game, landscaping or the effect on the farm

certainty and at a fraction of the price by releasing more hand-reared birds!

The general wildlife and landscape surveys (carried out by the Nature Conservancy Council and the Forestry Commission's Landscape Department) were very detailed and their suggestions extremely interesting because they very closely matched the requirements for improving the game. Wildlife and landscaping have, of course, no financial yardstick by which they can be judged – only strong aesthetic and moral justification. Unusually, it is the landscape and wildlife sectors which have come to the rescue of the game habitat and not the other way about. The management plan has now been considerably modified in their favour at an acceptable cost. (Details are published in Forestry Commission Forest Record 130, 'Thetford Forest Management Plan', published by HMSO.)

In a commercial forest, the forester is in an unenviable position. On the one hand, he is employed to manufacture trees in exactly the same way as others are employed to manufacture shoes or ships or sealing wax. On the other hand, he is subject to intense criticism by people, both professional and amateur, who understandably hold strong views on the effect of the 'tree factory' on the landscape and wildlife.

It was in my earlier survey in the north that I first came across this problem which resulted in the foresters being wary of giving too much and the game/wildlife/landscape lobby being equally wary of asking for too much. As a result we found ourselves standing in the middle of 5,000ha (12,350 acres) of moorland to be planted with Sitka spruce

over the following five years and passionately discussing whether we could make the rides a couple of metres wider than the forester had planned!

It is, I suggest, simply a matter of quantification. If the powers that be had the courage to say 'you can have a certain percentage' of the area then, and only then, can the non-commercial features of the forest be properly studied and planned. For instance, suppose the figure agreed was 5 per cent. I would first study the pattern of watercourses – rivers, small streams and, where present, drainage ditches – and see how much land would be used by leaving unplanted strips beside them of varying widths. If this could be done in a moorland area it could produce a natural linear structure on which more congenial habitat than non-native conifers could be planted or allowed to colonise.

Experts on deer control should be brought in at all stages. Red deer are likely to become a severe economic problem to the forests in the future and, since the only effective method of control is the high-powered rifle, the shape and aspect of the rides will affect its efficiency (and safety) in use. Similarly, fire precaution experts would need to be brought in to balance the value of additional means of access for themselves to control fire against means of access for the public, who are probably going to start a fire in the first place. This raises the question of water. Fishing is a very important section of the recreation industry and watercourses can be improved for both sport and fire control by damming to make small lakes and ponds or by using explosives to make pools.

As these new forests are on a fairly short rotation of around forty to fifty years (although, statistically, there is a 50 per cent chance that windblow may make it a good deal shorter!), there is no permanent loss

A typical moorland burn. All this ground as far as the eye can see is now planted with Sitka spruce. The area inside the black line should have been excluded from the planting

of timber production involved because if, at the time of cropping the trees, it was decided that 5 per cent was too generous then some or all of that percentage could be planted up with the next crop. But it would be better to err on the generous side when planning the first planting.

For pheasant shooting, some very attractive sport could result from this 'watercourse plan'. This would be particularly so where there is a pattern of small watercourses running in deep sheltered valleys down the sides of hills. It could be a wonderful young man's sport for two or three guns with Spaniels to drive birds to a similar number of guns standing below. If suitable habitat were encouraged, open to the sun but protected from wind, pheasants could be held in these areas which would be much more congenial than the surrounding desolation of the conifers.

The 'watercourse plan' has one immense advantage which outweighs all others and that is *flexibility*. A blanket of uncongenial trees sterilises the whole area for as long as the crop takes to grow – and forever if the process is repeated. The vein-like structure of the water-courses would keep the forest alive and would offer many benefits in addition to wildlife and sport. Walking and pony-trekking are additional activities to fishing and shooting but all those concerned must be accommodated, and camp-sites, caravan sites and log cabins are all possibilities as well as hotels and boarding houses. Farm shops and village stores would also benefit and the recreational activities could provide much greater direct cash increments to the local community than the forestry industry, which has not lived up to its expectations in this respect.

For the more formal type of driven shooting, a different use could be made of the 5 per cent. In, say, a 500ha (1,200 acre) forest seven game coverts of about 5ha (12 acres) each could be planted to provide a good day's shooting. These coverts would obviously be sited in the best positions to provide warm, sheltered habitat and high birds in the shooting season. You will have noticed that $7 \times 5ha = 35ha$ whereas 5 per cent of $500 = 25$! But the game coverts need not be unproductive of timber. They will need to have a substantial hardwood content – birch, alder, rowan, with a fair sprinkling of oak and beech where this is possible – but about one-third could be larch or Scots pine or a mixture of the two which could be used as a nurse crop for the hardwoods when planting.

This type of plan would probably be more attractive to the private estate than to the Forestry Commission. It would, however, be fairly expensive because it would be essential in most areas to exclude deer with high fencing until the trees were well established. In this respect there is a compensatory factor where deer control is concerned because they will always be attracted to the game coverts and thus provide a practical means of controlling the major portion of the population in the whole 500ha (1,200 acres) as well as producing a useful income.

For wildlife in general, this plan would be valuable because 5ha (12 acre) blocks of semi-hardwood forest, using native species and with a reasonable growth of ground cover, make viable units capable of sustaining their own population of many species of animal and plant life. When siting a covert, it would be particularly important to try to get one side, at least, adjacent to agricultural land and to try to link it with other coverts by rides or watercourses. This would further enrich the general wildlife and plant populations.

And so the 'tree factory' *does* hold promise for sport, wildlife and recreation, but attitudes must change before these promises can be fulfilled. It is no good planting the trees first and trying to fit these other features in afterwards; we have only to look at what has been done in the past to see that this does not work.

It is encouraging to see how intelligent foresters like Roderick Hewitt are planning on much broader lines than before. Certainly the Thetford Forest Plan has demonstrated how such planning can be economically viable in a large commercial forest.

What has been said applies to the Forestry Commission and the sporting landowner, but what of the absentee forestry investor? He is usually only interested in the fiscal benefits of planting trees; to him they are a set of figures on a balance sheet. Sometimes these forest owners, or syndicates of owners, have never seen the land they own or considered what the effect of their operations will be on wildlife and landscape. Often this type of ownership is very short term – buy in, plant under schedule D tax relief and with grants, sell out – all within five years or so. This type of operation is unfortunately inevitable in an industry which, because of its financial problems of longevity, has to be kept alive with fiscal benefits. Nevertheless, the threat of increased planning control imposed by central government has stimulated a more responsible attitude to 'investment planting'. This is to be welcomed since the involvement of urban planners – turning the countryside into a series of urban parks – would be potentially disastrous. The attitude of some of the more enlightened forestry contracting companies is very encouraging despite the problems they face in converting their investors. There is no financial return from wildlife and, where vast conifer blocks are concerned, precious little from sport.

6
Woodland Rehabilitation

Many people are discouraged from bringing their woodlands back into good management because the methods used in the past are now so costly. State aid in the form of grants are of limited use and the system of making them available on a fixed sum per hectare basis rather than on a percentage of cost is unattractive in the face of inflation and takes no account of the difference in costs between one site and another.

Nevertheless, it is the old system of clear felling, surrounding the wood with very expensive rabbit netting (or, even worse, deer fencing), planting with very small trees and then weeding annually for five years or more which deters so many people although, if finance is available, there is no denying that it is still the best system silviculturally.

This discouraging prospect has resulted in many acres of woodland remaining without any effective management and, even worse, the physical removal of a great many woodland areas (particularly small areas) previously of immense value to wildlife.

The clear-felling system has nearly always produced problems for the game manager because, in order to reduce fencing costs, the areas treated are usually fairly large. For a few years they can be useful as nesting areas (as long as provision is made for the chicks to go through the wire netting) and then, quite suddenly, they become impenetrable jungles harbouring nothing but predators and from which shot birds are difficult, if not impossible, to retrieve. This thicket stage can last for ten years or more and can effectively sterilise all or large parts of a wood from the sporting point of view.

Today, however, economic necessity has given birth to different attitudes and methods, and the basis of these is the use of large trans-plants 1.5–2m (5–6ft) high rather than the much smaller forest trees of the past. These larger trees, mostly referred to as 'whips', combined with plastic sleeves to protect the plants from rabbit and hare damage, are a practical method of restocking old woodland areas. (This system, incidentally, has recently been re-discovered by the professional foresters and given a fancy name – enrichment!)

The method of planting is simplicity itself. Obviously the trees must

An old neglected shelter belt. The Scots pine are probably survivors from hedges of that species. Rehabilitation with tree whips in protective sleeves and *Lonicera nitida* hedges would be simple and effective

have light to grow well and small gaps in the old tree or coppice canopy must first be made to form 'skylights' beneath which the new trees are planted. The whip and skylight method has a number of attractions to the private woodland owner:

1. It eliminates the capital cost of fencing and most of the early annual establishment costs.
2. There is no economy of scale. The cost of each skylight planting is the same whether one is making a single unit or a hundred.
3. This gives great flexibility since the number of units planted each year can be varied according to the finance and labour available, whereas after expensive clear felling and replanting there is an unavoidable commitment to continue annual management for at least five years if the operation is to succeed.
4. From the game point of view, it can have a dramatic effect by bringing a bare-floored, derelict woodland back to life in a couple of growing seasons, since in most woods a good sprinkling of evenly distributed skylights will soon show a dividend in excellent nesting and winter holding cover.

The system is best applied where there is a light stock of hardwoods, such as oak and ash with an understorey of dense overgrown hazel coppice. One sometimes sees hazel included in newly planted game coverts and there seems to be an idea in some people's minds that it is in itself of value to game. This is not so. It was, however, part of a *management system* that was of great value and that was 'coppice with standards'. Largely to be found in the southern counties of England, this was a light stocking of oak – about 50–60 to the hectare (20–25 per acre) – with an understorey of sweet chestnut or hazel coppice. The sweet chestnut coppice was (and still is) on a rotation of about fourteen to twenty years to provide fencing stakes, hop poles and, since it cleaves so easily, portable sheep hurdles and the type of fencing known as 'chestnut paling'. All except the sheep hurdles are still produced in large quantities. Hazel, on a much shorter rotation of six to nine years, was almost entirely used for close-woven sheep hurdles which are now only produced in small quantities for garden use. Hazel is tolerant of many different soil types whereas sweet chestnut is much more choosy. For this reason much greater use was made of hazel and this is why so many of our southern woodlands look so sad today with an understorey of overgrown and neglected hazel, its bare floor littered with dead branches.

Tree shelters protecting hardwood whips planted in a skylight cut into a derelict hazel coppice

The making of hazel hurdles is dying out. As a result shade from overgrown hazel coppice has caused the decline of many good game coverts

When sheep hurdles were in constant demand it was the management of the coppice which produced such attractive habitat for pheasants because the areas cut were usually fairly small and as a result the floor of a sizeable oak wood, for instance, was in all stages of development at once, with recently cut bare areas, middle-aged fairly thick brambly ones and the older sections with more patchy cover under a denser canopy. The litter and shade from sweet chestnut is more dense than hazel and in consequence the habitat it produces is not so good.

A further advantage of the coppice with standards system was that oak was usually the main crop which meant that, with their long growing period, the woods and their management remained stable for a great many years. And then, of course, sheep were replaced by cattle and arable, the hurdles by wire netting, and everything changed.

Skylights should not be too large for pheasants; 12–15m (40–50ft) in diameter is usually the right size in an old hardwood area with a fairly open canopy. If they are too large initially, this may promote a jungle of brambles which will be excessively thick for both the pheasants and the trees. For this reason it is important to study the ground carefully before rushing in with a chain saw. If there are any existing skylights in the wood note the kind of growth that results and if it is very dense then be wary of making the skylights too large. If you have a completely bare-floored wood do not be lulled into thinking that nothing is going to grow. If you can see one small bramble shoot with a couple of tiny leaves, this can become a dense thicket if given too much light. Always remember, therefore, that you can make your skylights bigger if you judge, after the first growing season, that they are too small, but you cannot make them smaller.

To create new skylights, follow this very simple and effective method. In January or February, go through the area with a bill hook and a large ball of bailer twine. Place the latter on the ground and, taking the end, walk around the area you want to make into the first skylight. Tie the end to a branch at shoulder height and go back round the area slotting the twine into notches cut with the hook, finally cutting it off and tying it to the branch where you started. This circle of twine, nowadays usually bright orange, is easily seen so that you can site each subsequent skylight in relation to its neighbours. The density of the sites depends on whether you wish to cover an area intensively or to have them fairly well dispersed and come back another year to make more in between. The planning should aim to produce one good tree from each skylight at the final distance for the crop – say 20–30m (22–33yd) for oak. If there are any promising young trees already growing in the areas to be cut they should be marked with a few twists of bailer twine. It is then a matter of telling the forester to cut everything inside the rings of bailer twine except the trees you have marked.

This planting system is obviously vulnerable to damage by roe deer but this can be minimised with care. First, the trees to be planted should be well protected with tree shelters or plastic netting to a height of *at least* 1.5m (5ft). These sleeves must be firmly stapled to a stout stake driven well into the ground. If this is not done the deer can lever the sleeves off with their antlers.

As a further precaution some of the lop and top (ie light branches) from the cut coppice should be piled around the trees, just leaving their leaders showing above. This material will rot away after a season or two but it should give a little extra protection in the first year when it is important to get the tree leaders growing well above the reach of the deer. Subsequent management should involve no more than replacing failures and even this may not be considered necessary because if one is planting four or five trees in the expectation of selecting the best one as the final crop then some failures are acceptable.

The initial growth rate from trees planted in this way will not be as good as following a clear fell. But if it means the difference between management and neglect, good sport and bad, then surely it is the right answer.

A problem with this system is that the cutting of the skylights is very labour intensive. If the coppice is large enough for firewood one can sometimes get the cutting done at no cost and even a small profit by a firewood merchant. An excellent alternative is to employ that splendid organisation, The British Trust for Conservation Volunteers. These energetic young people are well led and well equipped. Dealing with old coppice is one of their specialities. All they need is somewhere to camp (preferably a barn or similar building). They bring all their own tools and food.

RESTORING SMALL SPINNEYS AND SHELTER BELTS

The skylight and whip system is the obvious answer to bring these areas back to life because small areas, and particularly narrow belts, are prohibitively expensive to fence against rabbits and hares. Spinneys rarely have much in the way of valuable trees because these have usually been taken out in the past (as the most easily accessible) when the owner wanted a bit of cash or a good fence post or two. What is left is often misshapen and of poor quality and so there is usually no problem when it comes to felling a few trees to let in a bit of light and underplanting with whips.

However, before considering the centre of a spinney or belt, priority should be given to the perimeter. These small areas are extremely vulnerable to wind and so shelter at ground level is absolutely essential if they are to provide good game habitat. Quite often an old neglected thorn hedge is present, usually grown to 5m (16ft) or more in height and with large gaps close to the ground between massive old stems. The answer here is to cut them right to the ground since laying is not always successful and if you cut them at waist height, as one often sees done, they will simply grow from there leaving the gaps at the bottom as before. Once they are cut to the ground, *Lonicera* or more thorn plants can be planted in between the stems and allowed to mingle with the new growth. If the hedge is overshadowed by trees, there is a further problem because if these trees are cut in a small spinney or narrow belt you may have nothing much left at the end of

Tree hedges if neglected eventually grow out like this one in Norfolk

the operation. The logical answer is to steal a bit of ground outside and plant a new *Lonicera* hedge 5m (16ft) out from the old one. Before you become alarmed at this, it is worth noting that you would have to create 2,000m (2,200yd) of new hedge before losing 1ha (2.5 acres) of ground!

Small spinneys often contain coppice as a result of indiscriminate cutting in the past and it is worth considering continuing the coppicing as a source of fuel either for your own use or to meet the needs of the increasing number of enclosed wood-burning stoves. Ash is fortunately both reasonably quick to regenerate and an excellent fuel material.

A dense windproof perimeter hedge is essential for providing ground level shelter to a small spinney

Regular coppicing, even on a fifteen to twenty year rotation, such as one might establish for ash, will maintain good game habitat.

Old shelter belts can present slightly different problems because, although it should not be too difficult to restore hardwood trees by the use of whips, it is very often conifers that are needed and protective sleeves for these can be expensive if wire netting is used. Plastic netting is probably a better answer but it is still not cheap. In exposed positions, additional protection from wind can be very important in getting the young trees established and fertiliser bags can be very effectively used. They do not look very attractive but they need only be in place for a couple of years by which time the trees should be growing well. Replanting the edge of a belt also requires similar methods to protect the most suitable species such as laurel and *Cotoneaster* but sweet chestnut, being a hardwood, is easily fitted with the cheaper variety of sleeve.

How frequently one sees these little spinneys and old belts looking sad and neglected nowadays. Tragically, the answer is often the bulldozer, but a little cherishing and simple, cheap management can restore them to prosperity to the advantage of wildlife, game and the landscape. Do please think of this before you take drastic (and expensive) action to eliminate them.

7

Forestry Operations and Planting Small Areas

All forestry operations, such as planting, weeding, thinning and felling, can be a source of friction between forester and gamekeeper. This is quite unnecessary if the two understand each other's problems and work together. Keeper and forester should meet regularly to discuss and co-ordinate their respective plans, with the landowner or agent 'in the chair' whenever possible. If the two never meet except to disagree, neither will prosper and their employer will be badly served. Where an outside contractor is employed, the situation is likely to be aggravated by the fact that they have different employers and loyalties. But it is the estate owner who pays the bill – and should be allowed to call the tune!

The chief source of irritation seems to be based not on lack of sympathy but on lack of understanding. It is vital, therefore, that a gamekeeper should have some knowledge of forestry and the forester should know a little about game management – even better if he shoots. I have often urged people to try to persuade their farm managers to shoot – even if they risk getting shot themselves – because, once the farm manager is keen, the planting of game crops which has previously been 'difficult' or 'impossible' suddenly becomes routine! I think the same applies to foresters. If the different estate departments, including farming, remain in separate compartments, there is always trouble.

PLANTING

Planting distance varies greatly with the species, from 1×1m (3×3ft) for some hardwoods to 12×12m (40×40ft) for cricket bat willow. Most planting used to be done at 1.5×1.5m (5×5ft) spacing but now it is more likely to be 2.5×2m (8×6ft) allowing access for mechanical weeding. Other advantages of the wider spacing are the saving in the number of plants required, less early and uneconomic thinning, and less density at the thicket stage.

The Deer Hay Valley in 1964 (above) and in 1984 (below) after the author's planting

Certainly on good ground, where a large percentage of the planting can be expected to be successful, the wider spacing has much to recommend it. Not all species can be treated in this way; Scots pine, for instance, grows very poorly when widely spaced. However, there is room for experiment, and wide spacing would certainly make it easier to control predators and rabbits in the young plantation, make it more accessible to beaters and give room for pheasants to get on the wing.

Wherever possible, the rows of trees should always *run in the direction in which the birds are to be driven*. Foresters have a particularly perverse habit of getting this wrong. On one occasion I came across a small square wood where it would not have mattered if the lines had run from top to bottom or side to side. The genius who planted it ran them diagonally, the only way which makes driving pheasants virtually impossible and invariably results in the beaters arriving in a confused heap in one corner!

WEEDING

This can cause considerable friction between keeper and forester, particularly over the timing of the operation since the weeding and nesting seasons coincide. The peak date for pheasants to start laying is about mid-April, and for the start of incubation 6 May. The main hatching period is between 20 May and 20 June. Hens disturbed during the laying period usually re-nest shortly afterwards, and even if the nest is destroyed during the incubation period, there is a reasonable chance of the hen nesting again providing that she has only been sitting for a few days.

The most dangerous period is between 12 May and 20 June – just when the weeding operation tends to be in full swing. This is when consultation between forester and keeper is vital. Where several plantations are concerned, it is obviously best to weed those on the boundary, or with a lower density of hens, during the danger period. Areas where it is known that there will be a large number of nests should be left until later in the season.

This may not be possible, particularly where there are only one or two plantations on the whole shoot, but even here the losses can be limited by careful management. A system of rewards for nests found and left to hatch undisturbed can be very effective in opening the eyes of the weeders. The keeper should try to make time for a visit once or twice a day for a friendly chat. A show of gratitude at the right time can be worth its weight in gold – or pheasant chicks!

Mechanical weeding is now more generally used, although it is mostly confined to plantations on new ground because old stumps and coppice stools can damage the machinery and cause delays. This method can destroy a large number of nests, particularly with the type of machine that uses rotary blades or chain flails. The only answer is to cut more frequently so that the hens are encouraged to nest in the longer material close to the trees or in areas which are inaccessible to the machine. Chemical weeding can often be used where the sporting interest is high, but most plantings include broad-leaved species and control by herbicide is to some extent limited by their presence.

The successful use of herbicides in plantations requires meticulous attention to application rates and to the timing of the work and there are advantages to be gained from their selective and careful use. Spot or hand application in late winter or spring, either before or after planting, can give good control of weeds around the trees while retaining cover in the untreated area.

Plantations treated in this way will not require hand weeding during the nesting season, thus keeping disturbance to a minimum. Herbicides can also be used selectively against less welcome species to produce a ground cover more amenable to game; for example, by controlling *Rhododendron ponticum* and bracken.

The selection of herbicides available is wide and increasing every year and great care is required in the choice of the best one for your purpose. Management costs can be reduced by their use but it is essential to seek professional advice before using chemical control because of the potentially disastrous results if you get the treatment wrong.

Application may be by knapsack sprayer (with or without shield), granular distributor or controlled droplet applicator. As a guide, herbicides for use in a planted area are:

against grasses: atrazine, propyzamide and paraquat
against bracken: asulam
against woody weeds and mixtures: glyphosate

When planting on a virgin site, as opposed to a clear-felled area, the most pernicious weed is grass. Recent research by the Forestry Commission on the control of grass weeds came up with some extremely interesting facts. Trials were carried out on the effect of various weeding regimes on standard geans (wild cherry) which tend to react quickly to any checks on their growth. The regimes used were as follows:

1. Bare ground, ie eliminating all vegetation around the tree roots.
2. Grass cut once.
3. Grass cut twice.

4. Grass cut continuously like a lawn.
5. No control at all.

The effect on the tree growth in order of efficiency was 1, 5, 2, 3 and 4. It might therefore be thought that the most economical system would be no control at all! However, in field conditions the smothering effect of tall grass falling over the trees in the first couple of growing seasons should be taken into account and some action taken to avoid this. It would appear to be best, therefore, to use chemical spot weeding to clear all growth around individual trees and, if that is not practicable, then second best is to spot weed with a hook to clear overhanging grass.

Whatever method is used, some damage is almost inevitable. But careful management and good labour relations can reduce it to reasonable proportions. A keeper must accept this, at the same time taking some comfort from the fact that weeding will not go on forever, five years being about the normal span. He should also remember that he is very dependent on a reasonable acreage of well-managed woodland for a good pheasant yield.

THINNING AND CLEAR FELLING

These operations can have disastrous results for the keeper unless he is given plenty of advance warning, preferably twelve months. I once received a plaintive telephone call from a gamekeeper telling me that the forestry department had arrived to thin a plantation two weeks after he had turned a thousand pheasant poults out into it!

On several occasions I have seen timber left after felling and then drawn through the neighbouring wood in the middle of the nesting season. This has resulted from poor extraction facilities such as narrow rides where the vehicles quickly become bogged down forcing the contractor to wait for dry weather. Such difficulties can only be avoided if keeper and forester plan together.

'Lop and top' is a frequent source of trouble. In some cases this is because no proper agreement has been reached with the purchaser of the timber to remove or burn it. If it is left lying as it falls, the area can quickly become a jungle of old branches entwined with brambles, from which it is impossible to flush pheasants or control predators. If a wood is left like this for a year, the cost of clearing for replanting can double or treble. Owners should make certain that the contractor is bound by his contract to burn or remove all unwanted material as he goes.

This problem can also be created by gamekeepers and owners themselves where the wood is bare-floored and the lop and top is left 'to give a bit of cover'. This is often a mistake, but if it is considered advisable then it must be properly carried out. This involves laying the material in groups or rows with the butts towards the approach line of the beaters and the tops towards the guns. In this way pheasants that creep into the material with the 'lay' of the branches can usually be moved out by the beaters. If they go in 'against the lay' so to speak, they frequently become trapped, particularly when the brambles grow through. This also means that they are much more vulnerable to dogs and foxes. This system is probably best avoided, although if it is used under bare beech or conifer woods where there is no bramble growth that is a very different matter and it can be very effective as an aid to holding more birds or making flushing points. In the very small areas such as the skylights, previously described, there should be no problem.

RABBIT FENCING

The necessity for using wire netting to exclude rabbits and hares from a young plantation is a great nuisance to both forester and game manager. It is extremely difficult to keep secure, since one hole in a mile of fencing is enough to admit a breeding population, and very often rabbits are enclosed in the area when the fence is first erected; everyone knows how difficult it can be to get the last one, which is bound to be a pregnant doe!

As already mentioned, pheasants dislike netting because it prevents them from running in and out of the cover, but they will go in to nest. The fact that chicks up to ten days old can get through rabbit netting is no consolation if the growth of grass effectively blocks the meshes of the netting. When you see this in the spring do not be tempted, as I once was, to put a match to it or you will end up with a runaway fire! The best solution is to take steps to prevent some of this growth *as soon as the fence is erected*. A good herbicide such as Round-up or the longer lasting sodium chlorate should be used and it is best to apply it in short lengths of a couple of metres at intervals of 4 or 5m (13 or 16ft). The corners must always be cleared since it is here that chicks frequently congregate when trying to get out. Planks or logs sloping up to the corner posts inside the fencing make useful exits especially for older chicks that cannot get through the netting. Some people put turves on these ramps and this makes sense if round logs are used which do not offer very secure footing.

Some years ago I watched pheasants jumping onto the crossbar of a gate in a rabbit fence. Some paused to have a look around and others just hopped straight down on the other side. It was obviously a painless way of negotiating the fence without actually flying – just a couple of flaps of the wings and they were up and over. Since then, I have always recommended extending this facility by nailing light 'jump' poles across a few pairs of the fence posts around a plantation. It is surprising how quickly the pheasants will start using them, particularly young poults.

Pheasants are easily trapped against wire netting by predators, such as foxes and marauding dogs. I have even seen a stoat catch a twelve week old poult after chasing it for 40m (44yd) or more. In its panic the bird never attempted to fly and I think this is how some get taken against the netting. A useful practice is to place a few straw bales at intervals against the *inside* of the netting and these can act as stepping stones to help a bird up over the wire if it is being pursued. Pheasants certainly use them as a means of crossing the fence during their normal activities. Droppings on the bales also show how popular they are with pheasants for getting up off the ground to survey the area. (Bales in game crops, such as kale and mustard, are also valuable for this purpose.)

Farm machinery and cattle are the two most likely threats to the security of the fence. A tractor driver turning as close to the fence as possible can easily tear a hole in it without noticing. On one occasion I was shown where a diligent operator had gone along with a finger mower and neatly sliced through the netting for most of its length! A despairing gamekeeper once showed me a beautifully erected fence which was painstakingly fitted across the middle of the stump of an old oak leaving a convenient platform on each side to allow rabbits and hares to pop over. 'And they blame me for the rabbits!', he exclaimed.

Cattle, however, are probably the biggest menace. The normal rabbit fence is never strong enough to keep them out and so it is essential to put in really strong posts and three or four strands of barbed wire along the outside of the netting and an additional strand along the tops of the posts which should project at least 120cm (4ft) above ground. Even this is not always sufficient because when the cattle have heavily grazed their own side of the fence the grasses on the other side will be irresistible and, barbed wire or no barbed wire, they will push against it and force it to stretch. It then goes slack and the animals can start reaching over the top. In no time at all the fence is a shambles and rabbits can easily pass in and out and sometimes the cattle as well. There are two ways of solving this problem. If room is left for a tractor to pass between the fence and the newly planted hedge or trees, then this small area can be kept mown down tight, but this may have to be done more than once. A better and more permanent answer is to spray a 2m (6ft) strip inside the fence with a herbicide to kill out the grass. Both these methods will not only discourage the cattle from leaning over but allow pheasants and chicks to move around the perimeter freely. They will find it much easier to cross the fence if they are not pushing through a tangle of rank undergrowth to reach it.

SMALL AREAS OF COVER

I remember my father saying in the 1920s that if you saw a farm or shipyard that was tidy you could be sure that it was not making a profit. The opposite seems to be true today and anything that looks untidy or gets in the way of a machine on the farm is swept away on the principle that it is wrong to have anything that is not 'producing'. In two instances I have seen farmers destroy the habitat for a potential six-gun shoot on their land in order to achieve an addition to their gross income *before* tax, and then hire a single gun in a syndicate elsewhere which costs them more out of their net income *after* tax!

A lot has been done in the conservation world to try to get something put back to compensate for this destruction and much of this has been concerned with the preservation of the hedgerow structure and the planting up of small areas such as field corners.

Recent research indicates that hedgerows are probably of far more value to the farmer than has previously been realised and that they have an important part to play in the ecology of a modern farm, even though it may be purely arable and divided into much larger fields than in the past.

Hedgerows, small areas of uncultivated land, old pit holes and woodland edges are all capable of harbouring invertebrate populations that are of value to the farmer as predators of pest species and to the game manager as essential food for gamebird chicks.

In the modern cereal farm the most serious invertebrate pests at present are wheat bulb fly (*Leptohylemyia coaretata*), three species of cereal aphid (*Sitobion avenae, Metophlophium dirhodum* and *Rhopaposiphom podi*), the frit fly (*Oscinella frit*), thrips (*Limothrips spp.*), slugs (such as *Agriolimax reticulatum*) and leatherjackets (*Tipula spp.*). New ones develop with changing farm practices such as the cereal and grass fly (*Opomyza*) which is thought to have increased as a result of the tendency to drill cereal seeds earlier. This adds up to nine species but the total number of invertebrate species that occur on British cereal farms is about 800 and this is only a rough estimate since so little research has been done that the true number is not known and could be many more.

A considerable proportion of this huge total comprises species which prey on pests but the increasing use of unselective and deadly insecticides kills friends as well as enemies. As a rule it is the enemies which multiply at a tremendous rate in the vacuum produced by these sprays and the only places where the useful species are able to survive and over-winter is in the hedgerows, rough corners and so on, the very features which are being so ruthlessly torn out. The less habitat for friendly species, the more pest species; the more pest species, the more sprays; and so it goes on.

'Hedges only harbour rabbits' is another frequently heard cry. Some time ago I was passing through a farm which consists of two fields, each of approximately 150ha (370 acres), divided by the main road. In one of the fields three combine harvesters were working but a fourth was stationary and leaning over at an acute angle. During the following winter I met the owner when we were guests at a mutual friend's shoot and I asked him what had happened to the combine. 'It fell into a rabbit earth and broke an axle', he said. In fact, there were several large earths in the field but they were not seen because the field was so big until harvesting started and the combine drivers on their raised platforms began to notice them. One wheel of a combine, with a full tank, broke through the surface crust above a rabbit earth and that was how the accident occurred. I had the greatest pleasure in telling the owner that if he had had a few hedgerows he would have known where the rabbits were and could have controlled them! You will not get rid of rabbits just by removing features which they normally use for breeding; they will quickly adapt to new areas when the necessity arises.

However, it obviously makes sense to see that you *can* control the rabbits in these sort of areas if they are to be retained. Wide, overgrown hedges and uncultivated areas allowed to become impenetrable jungles are certainly not what the game manager requires; on the contrary, they are only havens for gamebird predators, as well as rabbits. A good nesting hedge, such as one sees growing on a low bank in West Norfolk, need only be 1m (3ft) wide and occupy a total ground width of about 2m (6ft). A partridge or pheasant will nest in the centre of this type of hedge and if a predator approaches from one side she can escape via the other. In a wide unkempt hedge the bird will nest at the edge with its back to the thick cover and thus only has one escape route – towards the approaching danger.

The only case for big hedgerows is where there is no other holding cover for pheasants and the hedge itself is wide enough to have a track cut down through the centre which can be used for winter feeding and predator control.

I have seen a number of plans produced for planting up field corners

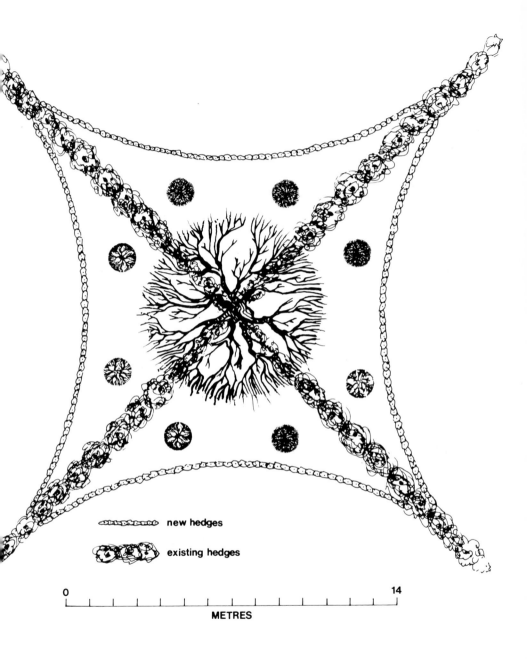

new hedges

existing hedges

0   14

METRES

Fig 22 Small Areas of Cover
The author's suggestion for a corner planting where four fields meet. Simplicity is the
keynote: one large tree, a few shrubs, new curved hedges will need little or no management and will not become a vermin infested jungle

127

but here two mistakes are frequently made. The first is to make them too elaborate with far too many plants, and the second is not to anticipate their visual effect on the landscape. As an extreme example, I well remember a farm in Scotland where the corners of the fields, which were divided by stone walls, had each been planted with four Norway spruce and when the trees were a few metres high the whole place looked quite ludicrous (rather like a child's model farm) punctuated by isolated trees which did not relate to anything in the surroundings. The choice of species was also peculiar since they would provide nothing except nesting and roosting sites for the local carrion crows.

If trees are to be planted in field corners, a few should also be planted in the hedgerows. This will avoid the danger of visually pinpointing the field corners. When planting the corners themselves, use the simplest possible layout, as shown in Fig 22 on p. 127. The existing hedge forming the cross at the centre could be left to grow tall and, if it is a very old one, it is probable that several species will occur apart from the main hedgerow plant which is likely to be hawthorn. Ash, field maple and crab apple are likely and other more shrubby types such as dogwood, blackthorn, elder and bramble may well appear. A new hedge defining the boundary of the area is important to prevent enthusiastic tractor drivers from ploughing the whole thing up again.

One tree is probably enough, depending on the size of the area to be enclosed. Fig 22 on p. 127 shows a minimum enclosed space 14m (46ft) square and one good oak tree will be just right to cover the area at maturity. Oak is a good choice because it makes a fine specimen as a solitary tree, produces acorns which pheasants and many other animals greatly enjoy, and has a far greater number of associated invertebrates than any other tree which grows in Britain. You might wish to put something in the spaces at the four corners, but do not be tempted to over-crowd them. One or two shrubs in each should be ample, although these spaces would be better left open to the sun and, provided the new curved hedges are kept tightly trimmed to give good ground-level protection from wind, these areas will be attractive as nest sites and for winter shelter.

When considering the use of field corners for game and wildlife it is interesting to see what they represent in terms of loss of cultivated land. In the first place, of course, it is land that is comparatively expensive to cultivate because of its shape. If they are kept to the size shown in Fig 22, then the amount of land lost on a 350ha farm divided into sixteen fields would total just under 0.5ha. In Imperial measurements, the loss on an 850 acre farm similarly divided would be just under one acre. The economic effect would therefore be negligible.

A typical marl pit. These are priceless assets as nesting cover for pheasants and partridges. Tragically many are eliminated in order to avoid a few minutes inconvenience for a tractor driver

Old flint, marl or gravel pits isolated in the middle of fields are priceless assets for game. They are off the main routes for ground predators and they can retain a useful insect population for any chicks hatched in them. Again, simplicity must be the aim of management. A perimeter hedge is not strictly necessary because shelter from wind is provided by the dip in the ground. A few berry-bearing trees or shrubs can be planted but it must be remembered that these sites are very susceptible to frost and the aim should be to leave the bottom unplanted and open to take advantage of any sunshine.

One often sees these old pits filled in but this usually leaves a scar in the field and frequently a damp patch. I know of one instance where an old flint pit, the only feature in a huge field and a regular successful nesting site for partridges, was bulldozed because it 'looked untidy' and was suspected of holding a rabbit or two. Subsequently, I was interested to hear that, although the corn drill fitted into the hollow that was left, the combine harvester did not and got well and truly stuck during harvest!

The author's game covert design planted on Lt Col Allhusen's Bradenham Hall shoot in West Norfolk. Notice how it is 'aimed' at the large home covert in the background. The site incorporates an old marl pit which can be seen on the lefthand side

There are still very many farms where small uncultivated areas continue to exist – the marl pits of Norfolk are an outstanding example – and intelligent land use must surely mean retaining as many as possible as likely allies in the war against insect pests if for no other reason. Once they come under purposeful management for biological insect control, game production and as landscape features, they seem to be readily accepted. If neglected they are all too often removed, although the result rarely justifies the expense involved. When bringing any small area under management keep to the golden rule: let the sun in, keep the wind out and make your plans simple. In this way little if any actual expense is incurred.

8

Game, Fish and Wildlife:
A Study in Compatibility

Every state in the USA has a 'game, fish and wildlife' organisation where the three areas are regarded as complementary rather than competitors as they still tend to be seen in Britain. This chapter aims to show how the three can be successfully combined even in a very small area if one plans the design with care.

First, select a suitable site, the best being a wetland area because it is invariably fairly rich and, of course, is the easiest where a water feature is to be included. It does not *have* to be in a river valley but only where the subsoil is impervious and will thus hold water when excavated.

In the valley of the Hampshire Avon, where I live, it is possible to find a suitable site almost anywhere, except where occasional flooding is a problem. Let us assume that you have a similar choice, namely level ground, alkaline soil and water with the water table about 1m (3ft) below ground level. Next, decide the main aims of the project. In this instance, let us assume that they are as follows, in order of priority:

1. a small farm reservoir
2. fishing
3. pheasant shooting
4. duck flighting
5. nature studies
6. a farm shop

Wildlife is not specifically listed because the aim will be to cater for wildlife in *all* categories and it will have equal priority with them (even the farm shop which could sell wildlife books, songbird winter feeding hoppers, nesting boxes etc).

Having jotted down the necessary information, make a rough sketch of how you want to construct and plant the area so that all these features knit together. Fig 23 on pp. 132–3 gives a typical design.

The first item to plan is the water area not only because it is the most important feature but also because there is much more to it than just digging a hole in the ground and hoping for the best. The most important aspects are as follows: (*contd on p. 134*)

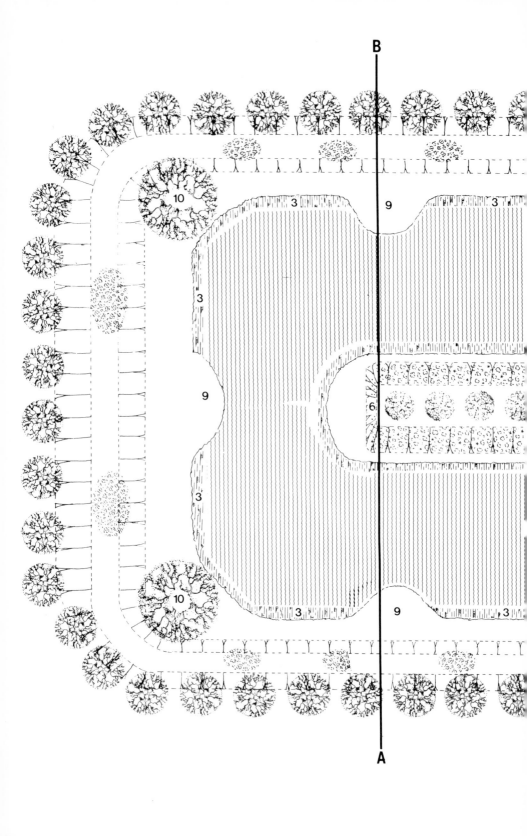

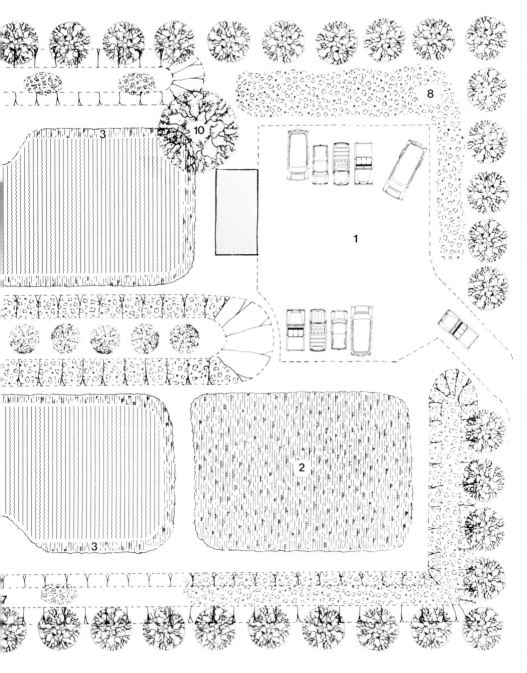

Fig 23 Amenity Areas
This diagram should be studied in conjunction with Fig 24. The various features are described from page 131 onwards and include: 1 car park; 2 small marsh area; 3 wet shelf areas; 4 pond; 5 peninsular spoilbank; 6 sand martin nesting colony; 7 perimeter spoilbank; 8 shrub bed for butterflies; 9 casting bays for fishermen; 10 weeping willows

- the size and shape of the reservoir
- the depth of the water
- the design of the spoil banks
- the water supply

The size of the area in Fig 23 is a purely arbitrary 100 × 60m (110 × 66yd) or 0.6ha (1.4 acres). But the spoilbanks may well pose a problem because, at the 6m (20ft) width shown, they would need to be at least 4m (13ft) high to accommodate the 4,500 cubic metres (4,950 cubic yd) that has to be excavated and it is not always possible to build up this height if the material is coming out very wet. If the excavation is drained with a pump whilst the work progresses, this can be a great help but it is always wise to allow extra room for the possibility of the banks spreading out rather more than you expected. An extra 10m (33ft) all round should be sufficient in the present case and this only amounts to another 0.3ha (0.75 acre), bringing the total to a round 1ha (2.5 acres).

The area of deep water will contain 285,700 gallons for every 1m (3ft) of depth. A suitable minimum depth for trout is 3.5m (12ft) and so the pond in this design should contain 1 million gallons when full. (If you need it any deeper, allow an extra 1m (3ft) of width to the outside spoilbank for each extra 1m (3ft) of depth.)

The horseshoe shape allows extra room for a central spoilbank and as long a bank length as possible which in turn adds up to a good long edge. This is important for the growth of marginal vegetation which gives cover for young waterfowl, autumn food from seeds and harbours important invertebrate food for both fish and fowl. The central peninsular spoilbank can be used to form an artificial cliff face at the outer end in which a sand martin nesting colony can be made.

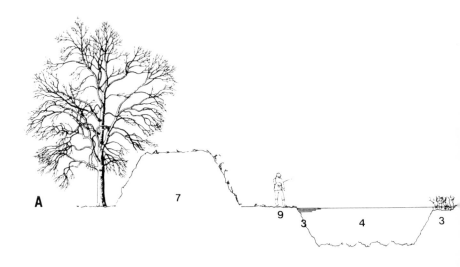

A   7   9   3   4   3

The water supply may come from natural seepage from the surrounding water table, pumping or by way of a nearby stream or ditch.
If the latter, be sure not to allow too great a flow through the pond
otherwise you will have a problem with silting. Cut a small inlet to
provide just the amount of water you require and, if necessary, put in a
simple hatch to shut off winter stormwater.

The ability to draw off water is very valuable for reasons other than
irrigation. First, it gives you much better control in the event of excessive weed growth and to remove surplus fish stocks or pest species.
Secondly, it enables you to expose an area of wet edge all round the
pond and even some of the bottom in the shallow area. This can bring a
dramatic increase in the number of visiting waders in the autumn.
(While managing the ARC/Game Conservancy Wildfowl Centre at
Newport Pagnell, I designed and had constructed a system of sluices to
enable the water levels of the wildfowl reserve lakes to be controlled.
During one three-month period when one of the lakes was gradually
being lowered, the number of visiting wader species increased to 14.) A
15m (16yd) section of the pond in front of the hut should be a shallow
area (0–30cm/0–12in) which can be used for this purpose as well as a
feeding place for mallard and teal in the winter.

A 1m (3ft) strip of marshy vegetation around the edge of the pond is
provided by a 'wet shelf' 30cm (12in) below the water level when the
pond is full and is a very important feature of good pond design. All
emergent water plants tend to be invasive but none will grow in 3.5m

---

Fig 24 Cross section of a composite wetland area designed for trout fishing, wildfowl,
game and songbird amenities. Other features include an aquatic plant display, a
miniature marsh study area, a sand martin nesting colony and a small butterfly garden.
See pp. 132–3 for key to this diagram

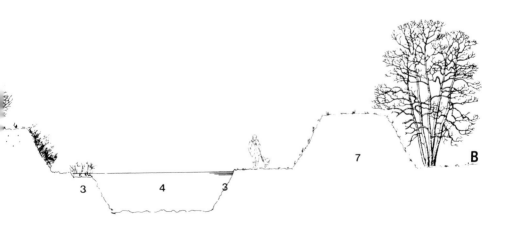

(12ft) depths and so they are confined to the wet shelf without need for management. (The species to be planted are discussed later.)

The half-round projections into the deep water are places where fishermen can stand to cast and land fish without disturbing the marginal plants. In a small design such as this there is insufficient room to allow for a full length back cast without getting caught up, but fishermen today tend to be a bit over-cosseted and a little extra skill in casting is not too difficult to acquire with practise and patience.

Next, decide on the best type of machine to excavate the pond. The maximum width is 12m (40ft) and so it is quite practical to use a hydraulic machine on tracks. If the width of water were greater, a dragline would probably be needed but even then it would be advisable to finish off the wet shelves and spoilbanks with the much quicker and more accurate machine. It is usually cheapest to hire a machine by the day rather than work on a contract price because a contractor will usually add a considerable sum for 'contingencies'. Nevertheless, if you put a machine on day hire any delays caused by difficult ground or sudden floods are your own risk rather than the contractor's. If you decide to contract the work, do get more than two quotes – you will probably be astounded at the difference in price!

With the main feature designed, next consider the type of building that you want. This will obviously vary with individual requirements, but the type of construction is extremely important whatever the size or shape. If the finance is available, a brick-built hut which can be securely locked is always advisable.

A stand of common reeds (*Phragmites*) exposed after lowering the water level. The normal water level would be 1m (3ft) higher

Starting from the car park, and proceeding clockwise, let us consider the other features in the design: a small marsh area which is very easy to make and can give you much pleasure. It is simply a pool with anything between 10cm (4in) and 1m (3ft) of water separate from the main pond. It is planted with the common reed which is why it must be away from the pond since this species of reed is very invasive. The main object is to provide a nesting scaffold for warblers, whose habitat these days is often threatened. But down below in the shallow water is a 'Tom Tiddler's' world of tadpoles, minnows and other small creatures that are the quarry of young children armed with jam jars and fishing nets. Such waters, if alkaline, are always rich in animal life and are the perfect site for introducing children to wildlife in miniature whilst at the same time making a useful contribution to the amphibian habitat.

DESIGN OF THE POND

Next we come to the pond itself with its all-important wet shelf at the edge. I am fortunate in that the water meadows where I fish are left entirely untouched by machinery or chemicals and therefore contain a wealth of wild plants from which to choose.

With so much choice, one can afford to be selective and pick those which give us pleasure as well as those which are valuable as scaffolds for the many types of insects one wants to encourage – from the larger types such as dragonflies down to the smaller creatures that spend their short lives pottering up and down the reed stems, some above water, some below, and some in both worlds.

My choice of plants – a simple selection but not always easy to find – would be as follows:

- Bur-reed, which has handsome flowers and spiky seed pods which provide food for waterfowl.
- Sea club rush, which is normally an estuarine plant but now found far inland as well. A prolific seeder and very elegant to look at, it makes a very pretty and long-lasting addition to a vase of flowers.
- Marsh marigold, the beautiful giant buttercup of the wetlands.
- Yellow iris, which is equally handsome and adds height as well as colour.
- Water plantain, a great favourite of mine with its delicate candelabra of flowers.

It is a mistake to overcrowd the planting, and only a few of the last three plants mentioned are needed to give the right contrasts in height and colour. Other plants will colonise naturally, such as the forget-me-not, comfrey and water mint with its sharp and refreshing scent. These will give you further pleasure.

Water plantain (*Alisma plantago-aquatica*)

Bur-reed (*Sparganium erectum*)

Marsh marigold or Kingcups (*Caltha palustris*)

The bottom of the pond should now be considered because during construction may well be the only chance you have of gaining access to it. If you de-water as excavating proceeds, you may well be able to run the excavator about on the bottom if the ground is firm enough; in any case, you can certainly see what the machine is doing.

The bottom gives us two important ingredients to a pond: a rooting area for submerged aquatic plants and a home for many species of insects. For fish, these insects provide food as they crawl about or swim to the surface where they attract the rising trout and, as they emerge, a very important source of high protein food essential to the diet and survival of ducklings.

The greater the area the more insects there will be, and so a rough 'ridge and furrow' configuration to the bottom will be much more productive than a flat one. Another refinement is to enrich the bottom with topsoil which will further increase the animal life as well as aid the plants.

Be very careful about planting anything on the bottom because many plants can be a great nuisance if they get out of hand. The most glaring example is probably Canadian pondweed which can completely choke a pond down to a depth of 4m (13ft) or more. It can arrive 'out of the blue', probably brought in on machinery or the feet of immigrant ducks. Since it is propagated vegetatively a piece only a few centimetres long is all that is needed to start the invasion. Coarse fishing is more tolerant of submerged weeds and others, such as the pondweeds, which rise to the surface, because the coarse fisherman's bait is static whereas trying to work a sunken 'fly' amongst them for trout can be very frustrating. Water lilies can be a beautiful addition but, again, they are very invasive. It is probably best to leave the bottom unplanted for two or three years and take what comes by chance before considering planting.

There is little room for trees or shrubs at the edge of a small pond because they are too much of a hindrance to fishermen and their shade will inhibit the growth of wet shelf plants. The peninsular spoilbank, however, does give some scope. A row of small trees or large shrubs along the top can add colour and be a source of food for pheasants and songbirds – perhaps a mixture of field maple and whitebeam or mountain ash. On the bank sides plant a combination of the low-growing creeping willow and woolly willow as well as some *Cotoneaster horizontalis*. This will make a colourful mixture of nesting cover for pheasants and ducks and excellent food and flushing cover for pheasants in winter. The top of the bank beneath the trees is a good quiet site for pheasants' winter feeding with easy access to a store in the hut or transport in the car park. If it is to be used for this purpose then plant holly or yew instead of the whitebeams or mountain ash. The reason for this is that the ground beneath the dense evergreen hollies and yews will remain clear of all but a very heavy snowfall and thus give pheasants access to food whether in hoppers or on straw that is placed beneath them.

SAND MARTIN COLONY

The main feature of the peninsular spoilbank is an artificial sand martin's nesting colony in a cliff face at the end (see Fig 24). If the spoilbank is by chance made of sand then it is only necessary to make the cliff face, packing it as tightly as possible with the excavator bucket but in any other soil the construction needs care. I am grateful to the British Trust for Ornithology for the following information which they kindly provided from their great store of knowledge.

The tunnels giving access to the nesting chambers need to be 1m (3ft) long, 8–10cm (3–4in) in diameter and preferably made of earthenware to give a good grip. There is nothing better for this purpose than the old-fashioned earthenware 'tile drain', which has a 10cm (4in) inside diameter and is about 25cm (10in) long. These can be laid end to end to make up the necessary lengths and there is no need to cement the joints because, when left open, they will assist drainage. The tunnels should slope downwards towards the entrance. The nesting chamber should be about the size of a grapefruit and so an earthenware flowerpot with a hole knocked in the side to fit over the tunnel pipe is a good object to use. (Do not use plastic pots which tend to sweat.)

The tunnel entrances should not be nearer the top, bottom or sides of the cliff face than 1m (3ft) which should discourage predators such as rats, stoats and weasels, and it is important to make the cliff faces as vertical as possible. The rows of tunnels should be about 30cm (12in) above each other and the entrances the same distance apart.

Start construction by making a platform 1m (3ft) above ground level, making sure that it slopes gently towards the face of the cliff (10cm/4in in the 1m/3ft length would be sufficient), and then lay the pipes out to form the tunnel so that the ends of the pipes are set back a few centimetres or so from the cliff face. As the pipes are laid down, they must be filled with sand because the martins appear to need to excavate this when first establishing the colony. There is no need to refill them each year because the birds return to the same nest hole annually. Next cover the row of tunnels and nesting chambers with well-packed earth and then construct another row and so on until you are 1m (3ft) from the top of the bank.

Turning now to the perimeter spoilbank and outside edge of the design, a compromise must be reached about shelter. The problem is that the fisherman needs some wind to ruffle the surface of the water and, if it occurs, to move blanket weed or algae to the bankside where it can be raked off. On the other hand, wildfowl, particularly those with young broods, need very sheltered water and pheasants, as we know, need good ground-level protection from wind.

The best solution is to set out the design on the ground so that the prevailing wind will blow at right angles to the peninsula which will provide good shelter to the downwind leg of the pond. The tree belt around the outside edge can be a combination of white willow to give tall shelter (and wonderful colours in summer and autumn) and common alder which can be coppiced for firewood on a fifteen to twenty year rotation to keep the trees fairly open and thus slow the wind to a gentle pace rather than trying to shut it out entirely. The two species should be planted alternately with 4m (13ft) in between. An alternative to white willow is cricket bat willow which can produce a very valuable crop but is not so attractive as the white willow (although it is a variety of it) and would need to be planted at 10m (30ft) spacing.

The spoilbank should be planted with groups of shrubs for two reasons: to form small flushing points for pheasants during the shooting season and nesting cover for both pheasants and wildfowl during the summer. The choice of species should be kept simple: red and yellow *Cornus* in pure groups and others a mixture of creeping willow, woolly willow and guelder rose. The spaces between the groups can be sown with meadow mixtures and individual species such as cowslip.

The two large trees at the waterside opposite the cliff face and the one by the hut are weeping willows which look so beautiful with their branches trailing in the water. It is worth remembering that trees are very important for the number of species of insect that they harbour, and native trees are much richer than exotics in this respect. The native oak, with over 200 species, is far and away the best, but the willow comes second with over a hundred.

To finish, there is the shrub bed beside the car park and this could be filled with different varieties of buddleia, the butterfly shrub. A suggestion for a mixture would be *davidii* 'White Cloud', 'Royal Red' and 'Black Knight' (which is a deep violet colour) with a background of *Buddleia alternifolia* with its long pale mauve flower stalks.

And so the design is complete. It is small and compact, but it demonstrates that it is possible to combine a great many features without conflict and that pre-planning is very important if you want to be sure of success.

9

Selecting Tree and Shrub Species

Before any attempt is made to select species for planting, certain conditions must be taken into account and they are as follows:

the soil — is it alkaline or acid, heavy or light, wet or dry?
the site — is it sheltered or exposed, is it in a coastal area or close to a city and subject to industrial pollution?
the climate — is it mild or severe in winter with high or low rainfall?

If you are not confident about the suitability of a species for a particular set of conditions, then it is always wise to take professional advice. The Forestry Commission can be particularly helpful concerning trees and the Royal Horticultural Society at Wisley, Surrey, on the choice of shrubs. There are also many books and commercial catalogues which have useful guides and none more so than Hillier's *Manual of Trees and Shrubs* (David & Charles) which is the best reference book on the subject for Northern Europe. It lists over 3,500 plants, with 600 illustrated in colour.

This chapter lists those species which should be considered for game coverts. The trees will be familiar to anyone with a reasonable knowledge of forestry, but for the shrubs I have listed some that would be worth trying as well as those in common use. However, the price of shrubs can very much depend on whether they are ordered in quantity and one should always bear this in mind before purchasing. Buying container-grown shrubs in twos and threes can be very expensive and it is cheaper to simplify your choice and order fairly large quantities — fifty or more — of a comparatively few species.

TREES

The 'commercial' content of a game covert will obviously be of prime importance when deciding on the trees to be grown and it will also greatly limit the choice. However, most covert planting today is on a reduced scale compared with the past, and the commercial content small or non-existent.

First, let us consider the size of tree to be planted. Commercial forest transplants are usually between two and four years old and commonly no more than 25cm (10in) in height. They are produced in enormous quantities in highly mechanised nurseries and as a consequence are very cheap. In order to prosper in a highly competitive market, commercial forest nurseries must produce very good quality plants and the most obvious feature to be seen is the root structure which must be fine and healthy.

Sometimes the seedlings' roots are covered with a small quantity of peat and rolled into paper 'Swiss rolls' so that they eventually grow flat root systems which are easily fitted into a slit made in the ground by a spade. With such small plants liberties can be taken with the roots if they are well developed.

Plantsmen would probably agree that these small trees will normally outgrow bigger transplants given time, but there are two problems which have been encountered fairly recently. The first is the very considerable cost of protecting such small plants from competition from weeds and damage by animal pests. The second snag concerns those people who are planting on a small scale. Most large forest tree nurseries find it uneconomic to market small quantities of plants, 1,000 being the usual minimum they will consider as it requires just as much paperwork to sell ten plants as it does to sell 1,000.

As a result of this, more and more small-scale plantings are being made with larger transplants of hardwoods at fairly wide spacing and with little or no conifers, as conifers are very unreliable to establish as large transplants and cannot be fitted with cheap, close-fitting plastic sleeves which effectively protect hardwoods from damage by hares and rabbits. The alternative has been to use netting sleeves which are expensive and make it extremely difficult to protect the plants from weed growth. The very promising new tree shelter system can greatly accelerate the growth of young transplants, while giving them good protection from roe deer as well as rabbits and hares, but for our purposes this produces another problem. The lower branches, closely confined in the shelters, tend to die off quickly so that the trees have naked stems much as though they had been hand-pruned. However, this is not an insurmountable problem if one knows it is going to happen; one simply has to accept that ground shelter must be provided by shrubs from early on and that this system of planting cannot be used for making conifer hedges.

With hardwoods, large transplants are perfectly practicable but their limitations should be remembered. As a rule, the larger the tree the longer it will 'sit' after planting before it starts to grow again. People often plant much too big a tree through impatience and this

144

never pays. Always plant the *smallest* tree that is possible, which with a sleeve would be just above the height of surrounding weeds or the reach of roe deer. Because of their comparatively slow growth, the whips of some hardwood species such as oak can be fairly expensive, but tree shelters used with small transplants have largely solved this problem. The results from the Forestry Commission's Research Division trials with oak are quite outstanding. Starting with very small plants (one year seedling and one year transplant) 22cm (9in) high, the controls with no shelter grew to 34cm (14in) by the end of the second year, whereas those in tree shelters reached 132cm (53in). Stem diameters started at 4.1mm (1.7in) and grew to 5.4mm (2.2in) in the control plants and 7.8mm (3.2in) in those with the shelter. Once the trees are clear of the shelter the growth appears to slow to about the normal rate. Of course, the initial cost is higher with the added expense of the shelter, supporting stake, fastening staples and extra labour, but this must be balanced against the lower cost of the small plants and a higher success rate of establishment. We are probably only at the beginning of development of individual tree protection systems and it is to be hoped that methods and costs will improve as time goes on.

Meanwhile, there are other things to be taken into consideration when using large transplants. The preparation of the site is important. If holes can be dug for the trees well in advance of planting this will be a great advantage. Where possible, this should be done in October ready for planting in January/February. Find out from the nursery what the expected diameter of the tree roots will be and the depth of planting and then make the holes twice as wide and twice as deep, breaking up the bottom to the depth of a fork. Exposure to winter frosts and the air will be beneficial. If possible mix 50 per cent peat and soil to fill in the hole when planting since this will stimulate root growth.

When choosing a nursery from which to obtain plants, remember that if the plants are very cheap they can be suspect. They may be reduced in cost because they have been in the ground too long and their roots are crowded and stunted. This often results in severe root damage when lifting and sometimes all the roots are growing in one direction like a bunch of bananas. A respectable nursery will never send out plants like this but, unfortunately, there are some that rely on tempting people with what seems at the time to be a bargain but which often leads to very disappointing results. Remember the basic rule: you plant the *roots* – not the tops!

Staking often presents problems. With polythene or plastic netting tubes, there should be no difficulty because the tube supports the trees and the stake supports the tube. It is when the stake directly supports

Layflat polythene tubing makes a useful low cost tree tie that needs no adjustment as the tree grows. The tree should be fastened as near to the top of the stake as possible to prevent chafe

the tree that difficulties arise. Large trees of 4–5m (13–16ft) high have stems of sufficient diameter to use plastic straps to fasten them to the stakes but this is never satisfactory with whips and can be positively damaging. Straps should always fit tightly enough to prevent the trees moving about inside them otherwise the tree will chafe and the bark will be broken. This can result in the tops dying or wounds which heal over temporarily and cause a break some years later. This type of damage can also be caused by fastening the tree too far below the top of the stake allowing the two to rub together in strong winds. The stem diameter of a whip at the top of the stake may be no more than one's finger, and it is usually not possible to tighten the straps sufficiently.

A satisfactory answer to this problem, however, is to bind the tree firmly to the top of the stake with layflat polythene tubing. This is simply polythene tubing which is of medium strength, pressed flat and made up into rolls, usually 100m (330ft) long. A convenient width is 10cm (4in). This layflat tubing is readily obtained from the large companies which supply home freezing materials. Be generous with it since it is very cheap to buy and a fraction of the cost of using ties. Use about 1m (3ft) at a time, wrapping it several times round the stake to form a cushion before tying in the tree as tight as possible to prevent any movement. There is no need to loosen the tubing as the tree grows because it will expand. Tree ties must be loosened regularly to avoid constriction and this is extremely tiresome because they become stiff and brittle with exposure and as this makes them difficult to adjust one usually finishes by making them much too loose and allowing chafe. Layflat tubing may not look as tidy as a tree tie but it is very practical and much, much cheaper than any other method.

Finally, there is the choice of species to plant. If you follow the principles in the design of a good game covert described earlier, you will first be looking for good shelter species for the perimeter area to keep out the wind, and this will mean conifers. In the centre of the covert you will want as much sunshine as possible and this in turn will mean hardwoods and none is better than the oak. Obviously, soil, site and climatic conditions are all important when making a final selection because unsuitable species will not prosper.

The choice of tree species is much easier than shrubs, but when you have made your choice it is a good idea to take a walk among mature trees of the species you propose to plant and remind yourself of their effect on their surroundings, and particularly on the *ground* beneath them. You may well find that you will go home and amend your final list!

Warning
Where apples and pears are grown Fireblight, which is caused by the bacteria *Erwinia amylovora*, can cause great damage. Host species for the disease are found in many of the *Rosaceae* family and, apart from apple and pear, the commonest are hawthorn, *Cotoneaster spp.* (particularly the larger species), *Pyracantha spp.* and common white-beam. Swedish whitebeam appears to be immune in England and mountain ash is rarely infected. There are, of course, plenty of other species to choose from in the lists which follow.

HARDWOOD TREES FOR GAME COVERTS

Alder *(Alnus)*
Although of little value as timber, the alders are welcome in a game covert and in wetland areas. Their seeds are eaten by pheasants and duck. They can be left to grow on as tall trees or coppiced and kept lower. The most commonly used are *A. glutinosa*, common alder; *A. cordata*, Italian alder; and *A. incana*, grey alder, which is the hardiest. They are best on heavy and wet soils but *cordata* will also do reasonably well on chalk.

Ash *(Fraxinus excelsior)*
A good timber tree which does well on moist sites and is tolerant of all soils including chalk. It is very useful if mixed with beech to produce a more open canopy. It coppices well and as such makes the very best firewood. Pheasants do not appear to eat the seeds.

Beech *(Fagus sylvatica)*
An obvious choice for chalk sites but its dense canopy and slow-rotting leaf carpet combine to produce a sterile floor. Once this has occurred nothing can be done other than felling selective trees to let in some light and even this can have disappointing results in an old wood with a crop of tall trees. When planting beech it is essential to underplant with *Prunus laurocerasus* (the common laurel) or *Buxus* (box) which will live under deep shade. It is essential to carry out this underplanting well before the beech canopy closes otherwise it will not establish. Beech seed is eaten in great quantities by pheasants.

Birch *(Betula)*
The seeds are eaten by pheasants and its light canopy allows a good growth of ground cover. Of little use for timber but it is a very handsome tree and makes excellent firewood. A few should be included in a hardwood mixture. The two commonly used are *B. pendula*, the silver birch, and *B. pubescens*, the white birch. There are numerous ornamental varieties, remarkable for the variations in colour and in the texture of their bark.

Cherry *(Prunus)*
The shrubs in this family are listed in the shrub section. There are two tree species that are also of value. *P. avium*, the gean or wild cherry, makes a very fine tree which occasionally includes a valuable veneer specimen. It is extremely useful on the perimeter of a covert and at the ride sides because it has a light canopy even when it grows to a large

tree and therefore throws little shade, and the added possibility of a valuable veneer specimen in the future makes it well worth planting a row or two. *P. cerasifera*, the cherry plum, is a complete contrast. It is a low, bushy tree which often produces a heavy crop of small fruits which are delicious to eat even though they need almost their own weight in sugar to enable you to do so! They also make very good jam. The place to plant them is also the ride sides and the edge of the covert where they can get some sun. Both trees are good on all soils including chalk.

Crab tree *(Malus)*
M. sylvestris, the common crab apple, is widespread in Britain. Pheasants enjoy the seeds or pips of most apples, including the crab, although they do not seem to eat much of the pulp. The fruits of the ornamental crabs vary in size and some are as small as the berries of the *Crataegus* or *Cotoneaster*. *M. floribunda*, *M.* Golden Hornet and *M. hupehensis* are the ones I use most frequently but there are many others to choose from. Like *Crataegus*, they are good medium-height trees to plant around the edge of a covert.

Holly *(Ilex aquifolium)*
A familiar native plant which makes an excellent warm roost for pheasants. It is, of course, very slow growing but it is always worth planting a few in a game covert, particularly at the ride sides where its dense evergreen canopy can protect a feed patch from snow. In addition to the common holly, there are fifty or so ornamental varieties to choose from. It will grow on most soils, but not well on chalk. It tolerates shade very well.

Lime *(Tilia)*
Another tree which has no direct benefit to pheasants but which adds character to a covert. *T. europaea*, the common lime, with its whiskery growth, can harbour undesirable predators and so *T. cordata*, the small-leaved lime, is probably preferable. Good-quality trees are often much in demand for wood carving. They make a good choice to grow on ride sides where their sweet scent is best appreciated.

Maple *(Acer)*
A large family with many sub-species and varieties, including the spectacular Japanese and North American varieties. For game coverts there are only two which I would use, namely *A. campestre*, the native field maple, and *A. platanoides*, the Norway maple. Neither gives any direct benefit to game but they are excellent subjects for improving the landscaping of coverts. The beautiful autumn colours of field maple

make a handsome addition to a woodland edge. Norway maple also has fine colouring as well as being a useful forest tree. I would never plant *A. pseudoplatanus*, the sycamore. It regenerates so vigorously that it eventually dominates everything and leaves a bare, cold floor blanketed with a dense layer of leaves. A sprinkling of Norway maple in a mixture of hardwoods should not cause any trouble. Both Norway and field maple will grow on chalk, and for this reason they are a useful alternative to beech.

Mountain ash *(Sorbus aucuparia)*
See whitebeam.

Oak *(Quercus)*
A favourite of nearly everyone except, it seems, the commercial forester. It has certainly been the basis of all our best game coverts in the past. Long lived and harbouring a rich understorey of shrubs and herbs, it encourages all the most desirable features for pheasants as well as a huge variety of other forms of wildlife. Wherever possible, oak should be the dominant crop of a game covert. *Q. robur*, the common oak, is the main choice but a sprinkling of the others should be added for variety, and these are *Q. rubra*, the red oak, which is initially much faster growing than *robur*; *Q. cerris*, the turkey oak; and *Q. coccinea*, the scarlet oak. Remember though, that *robur* makes the best timber. It is not often appreciated that oak is very tolerant of a wide variety of soils and aspects. It may not be the best timber tree in some areas, but it will nearly always grow there. The acorn is probably the first choice of tree seeds for pheasants and certainly it is for mallard.

Oleaster *(Elaeagnus angustifolia)*
This small tree is commonly called the Russian olive in North America where it is frequently seen as a medium-height edge species for shelter belts. At first sight it could be mistaken for a willow since the narrow silver leaves are similar to many willows. It can make a very handsome contrast to dark conifers and is certainly very hardy in North America.

Poplar *(Populus)*
The regimented rows of hybrid poplars planted for the match industry over the past thirty years are not very attractive, and now that they are no longer needed for matches (inevitably just as most of the post-war plantings are maturing) they are difficult to market. However, a

few *P. alba*, the white poplar, are a useful addition to a game covert because they have a mild suckering habit which produces a bit of cover and their white woolly leaves make a fine sight, particularly when moved by the wind. A few planted on the outside row of a perimeter shelter belt break the monotony of evergreen conifers.

Southern beech *(Nothofagus)*
An introduction from South America, this is now probably the fastest growing hardwood in Britain. A growth of 13–14m (43–46ft) in fifteen years is not uncommon in the higher rainfall areas of the west. As a timber tree, it is still very much in the trial stage for the simple reason that it has not been growing in Britain on a forest scale for long enough to assess its quality at maturity. Although related to our native beech, it does not share its liking for chalk. It throws a useful amount of seeds, but so far no one seems to know whether pheasants will eat them, but my guess is that they will. The growth rate can be spectacular and I have seen it in Northern Ireland way above the larch which was planted to nurse it! For this reason it is worth including a few in a game covert. The two most successful varieties in Britain to date are *N. obliqua* and *N. procera*.

Sweet chestnut *(Castanea sativa)*
The seeds are a great favourite of pheasants and for that reason alone sweet chestnut should be planted where it will grow. It is, however, rather choosy about its soil requirements, a dry, medium loam being the best. It dislikes chalk and too much wet. Although it is of doubtful value as timber, due to its tendency to shake when felled, it makes the very best coppice. Because it is so easy to split and cleave, it is still the basis of a prosperous cleft fencing industry as well as being extensively used as poles in hop gardens. It also makes first-class fencing stakes. It is a very good species to use in the rising area in front of a flushing point because its commercial value as coppice enables it to be kept low – about 5–6m (16–20ft) at its maximum.

Thorn *(Crataegus)*
C. monogyna, the common hawthorn, makes a valuable small tree which produces a good seed crop for pheasants who also like it as a night roost. There are, however, other varieties which have been developed for garden use but which make excellent subjects for a game covert, particularly on the outside edge because they are all of medium height, rarely exceeding 6–7m (20–23ft). *C. prunifolia, C. x lavallei, C. crus-galli* and *C. oxyacantha* can all be recommended. They all fruit well and *prunifolia* also has beautiful autumn colouring.

151

Walnut *(Juglans)*

Of no direct use to game, but why not plant one or two to give variety to the covert, and possibly provide your great-grandchildren with a very valuable veneer tree? The best varieties are *J. regia*, the common walnut, and *J. nigra*, the black walnut.

Whitebeams and mountain ash *(Sorbus)*

The two most commonly used whitebeams are *S. aria*, the common variety, and *S. intermedia*, the Swedish variety. Both have prolific crops of berries, which are readily eaten by pheasants. *S. aucuparia*, the mountain ash, also berries well and its clones, Joseph Rock *x kewensis* and *sargentiana* are favourites of mine for their extra berries and fine colours. *S. torminalis*, the wild service tree, is always worth including when considering varieties of *Sorbus*.

Willow *(Salix)*

Much of the willow family remains unclassified, but there are known to be many sub-species and varieties, perhaps 400 or more. It is a much underrated tree both in the game covert and the garden. It has an astonishing variety of shapes and sizes in the trees and its leaf, as well as stems of almost every colour in the spectrum. Obviously one tends to think of it as a wetland tree but it will grow almost anywhere. If coppiced every year, the new stems grow for their full length in their true colours. The willow is a fascinating species to study with the added incentive of extremely easy and cheap propagation from cuttings. The following varieties are selected as a good beginning for a collection around, perhaps, a flight pond or lake as well as including in covert planting.

Large trees
S. alba, the white willow, narrow silvery leaves, beautiful in summer and autumn.
S. fragilis, the crack willow which has brittle twigs which break off with a distinct 'crack', its bark is deeply grooved and the leaves shiny.
S. alba chermesina, the scarlet willow. Its orange/scarlet stems make it very showy in winter.

Medium trees
S. alba vitellina, the golden willow which has bright yellow stems.
S. x chrysocoma, the golden weeping willow. This is the best of the weeping varieties with yellow stems and narrow green leaves.
S. pentandra, the bay willow. The bright green bay-shaped leaves are aromatic when crushed.
S. tortuosa, an amusing variety with curled branches and twigs.

Small trees
S. *caprea*, the goat willow. The male has large yellow spring catkins, the female (also known as the pussy willow) has silver catkins.
S. *daphnoides*, violet willow. The purple shoots have an attractive white bloom.
S. *exigua*, the coyote willow has slim, grey-brown stems and silver, toothed leaves.
S. *viminalis*, the common osier is still used for basket making. It has long, green and silver leaves and grey, woolly stems.

CONIFERS

The following species allow the growth of some ground cover beneath them.

Corsican pine *(Pinus nigra maritima)*

Evergreen but usually a better timber species than Scots pine with a faster growth rate. This can be seen in Thetford Forest where the two grow in adjacent compartments and the superiority of Corsican is obvious. It is marginally better on chalk than Scots pine but otherwise it is similar to its requirements and its effect on ground cover. Also a good nurse species for hardwoods, but its faster growth may require slightly wider spacing to keep the hardwoods free in the early stages of growth.

Dawn redwood *(Metasequoia glyptostroboides)*

A deciduous variety that grows well in wet and swampy sites as well as dry ones. It is reasonably tolerant of chalk. It is a handsome tree not often grown but one which has similar advantages to larch in a game covert.

Larch *(Larix)*

Always desirable in a game covert where a high proportion of conifers is needed. Larch, being deciduous, makes for a much warmer conifer wood in winter time and will allow many shade-bearing shrub species to grow below, particularly brambles. The common forest varieties used are L. *decidua*, the European larch; L. *x eurolepis*, the hybrid larch; and L. *kaempferi*, the Japanese larch. They will grow in most soils and are reasonably tolerant of chalk providing it is not too shallow. They will grow in exposed sites but in this situation they are best screened from wind by evergreen conifers when they are much favoured for roosting by pheasants.

153

Mountain pine *(Pinus mugo)*
A rather slow-growing evergreen species which has a useful bushy habit. In young trees the lower branches sweep the ground and make good warm cover for pheasants on a cold site. It has been used very effectively in game coverts in Denmark. Like the Scots pine, it will grow on most sites. As I have only seen young trees growing, I do not know what effect they will eventually have on the growth of ground cover but I would think it would mostly be eliminated. Nevertheless, they could easily be coppiced and grown as low bushes and thus produce good cover themselves. They can certainly make quite a good hedge if kept trimmed to 2–3m (6–10ft).

Scots pine *(Pinus sylvestris)*
A native British conifer which tolerates virtually every type of site: cold and exposed, wet or dry, chalk or acid. Although it is evergreen, and can suppress ground cover for a number of years after establishment, the cover comes back as it grows to maturity. It is a good nurse species to mix in with hardwoods when planting a game covert.

Swamp cypress *(Taxodium distichum)*
A deciduous species generally regarded as the best conifer for wet or swampy sites, but not such a handsome tree as the dawn redwood. It does not like chalk.

The following species are evergreen conifers which normally suppress all ground cover. Their use in game coverts is confined to their effectiveness in providing shelter from wind, roosting for pheasants and as a nurse for hardwood species in new plantations.

Douglas fir *(Pseudotsuga menziesii)*
Probably the tallest growing conifer in Britain, with many fine specimens over 35m (115ft) high. It needs good soil, no chalk and is not happy on an exposed site where windblow may cause problems. It is of no real use in a game covert except as a roost and there are other and better species to choose for this purpose.

Giant fir *(Abies grandis)*
The most commonly planted of the silver firs. It requires good, moist soil and, although it will tolerate some chalk, it is not a good choice for alkaline sites.

Lawson cypress *(Chamaecyparis lawsoniana)*
A very good tree for a perimeter shelter belt around a game covert. It is

154

not ideal for roosting because pheasants seem to have difficulty getting into its dense branches which, in any case, tend to slant upwards rather steeply. I have sometimes seen Lawson planted along the sides of rides with the disastrous effect of turning the ride into a dark, sunless corridor. Incidentally, it is easy to distinguish Lawson cypress from western red cedar at a distance because the leading shoot of Lawson bends over, whereas the cedar remains erect.

Leyland cypress *(Cupressocyparis leylandii)*
This fairly recent hybrid is the fastest growing conifer in Britain but, because it is more difficult to propagate, it is usually more expensive than Lawson cypress or the western red cedar which it resembles. It is remarkably tolerant of every type of soil and good in exposure. Excellent for the perimeter shelter belt but, like Lawson, Leyland cypress is of little use for roosting.

Norway spruce *(Picea abies)*
The well-known Christmas tree makes good shelter and roosting. One frequently sees groups put into a rather draughty wood 'to warm it up'. It certainly produces some ground-level shelter initially but soon grows away leaving the ground beneath even more sterile and draughty than before. However, groups planted in an old hardwood covert can greatly improve it for roosting. Choose a good open space or make one by felling a few trees, and make a circular fence with a 50m (55yd) roll of rabbit-netting. Plant up with Norway spruce at 1.5 × 1.5m (5 × 5ft) spacing. Remove three-quarters of the trees after three to four years and sell them as Christmas trees which, with a bit of luck and skilful marketing, will pay for the plants and fencing. The remaining trees can grow on as a roost. Norway spruce is good in most soils but not on chalk or very dry ground.

Sitka spruce *(Picea sitchensis)*
Huge areas of Britain have been violated by this unattractive tree! The only way it is useful for game is as a hedge when its sharp, aggressive needles can make it impenetrable. It will need to be trimmed at least every other year to keep it as a hedge and it will probably not be very long-lived if treated in this way. A large plantation of Sitka will harbour nothing except predators to prey on your neighbours' game and there is a 50 per cent chance that it will blow down long before it reaches maturity.

Western hemlock *(Tsuga heterophylla)*
Only planted on an extensive scale quite recently and, of the dark

conifers, my favourite. Its horizontal, feathery branches make good roosting and it is a very handsome tree. It is also good under shade which makes it particularly suitable for underplanting roosting groups in old hardwood coverts.

Western red cedar *(Thuja plicata)*
Very similar to Lawson cypress but probably marginally better on chalk. It is also a good hedge plant.

Yew *(Taxus)*
Obviously not a commercial species, but well worth including in a hardwood mixture, particularly on chalk soils where it thrives. It is very slow growing, but it lives to a great age and prospers under the deep shade of beech. The leaf, particularly when it has fallen and dehydrated, is very poisonous but the berry is not and is frequently eaten by pheasants. It is wise to keep yew well away from the edge of the covert where farm stock might reach it. It makes a good roosting tree. *T. baccata* is the common yew. Do not plant *T. fastigiata*, the Irish yew, because its erect (ie fastigiate) growth makes it useless as a roost.

SHRUBS

There is no doubt that the most neglected aspect of covert planting is the shrub layer and yet it is the most important feature for pheasants. An old woodland site will usually develop a suitable selection of indigenous species naturally, but when planting on a new site it can be a very long time before shrubs appear. Two of the commonest species to do so in lowland Britain are brambles and hawthorn, probably because they have such prolific crops of berries whose seeds are carried to new sites by birds. Nevertheless, plantations can remain uncolonised even after thirty years!

It is always wise to accelerate the natural process when establishing a covert on new ground but the choice of plants must not only depend on the basic features of the site already mentioned – soil, aspect and climate – but also on the species of trees to be grown. The more open the tree canopy, the greater the selection of shrubs available. For instance, if you are planting pure spruce, Douglas, cypress or any other dark conifer it would be a waste of money to plant shrubs beneath them but the edge of the covert should give you the opportunity to include a few. On the other hand, a mixture of oak and ash with a nurse crop of pine and larch will give you much better scope.

Shrubs should always be planted so that either singly or in groups they cover an area about 5m (16ft) square *at maturity*. Examples would be four *Lonicera nitida* in a square at 2m (6ft) spacing or twenty *Hypericum* at 1m (3ft) spacing or a single laurel. Since the object is not to produce a solid carpet of cover but sporadic groups to maximise the edge effect, the distance between the groups should be about 20m (22yd) so that the density is approximately twenty-five groups to the hectare or ten to the acre.

Some people may prefer to delay planting shrubs until a couple of years after the trees have gone in and then replace any of those that have failed with shrubs, but it is probably better to put all the plants in at once – a delay in planting the shrubs might become permanent.

When making a list of suitable species, be more adventurous than our predecessors who tended to stick to just a few, such as snowberry, *Mahonia* and box for low cover and laurel and *Rhododendron ponticum* for larger species. *Rhododrendon* was a particularly disastrous choice which blighted many areas with its dense and impenetrable growth, but a lot more is known about the spread of non-native plants today, and only snowberry appears to be suspect. Even so, it is fairly easily controlled or even eliminated by modern shrub-killer sprays, unlike *Rhododendron*. Incidentally, game management is by no means entirely to blame for the spread of *Rhododendron*. In many instances the trouble stemmed from planting the more spectacular flowering species. These were often grafted onto *ponticum* stock which subsequently swamped out the graft. *Ponticum* also seeds freely and on the Island of Islay, off the west coast of Scotland, I have seen it spreading into neighbouring fields like thistles. It was an easy mistake to make since a combination of a fine *Rhododendron* collection and a good holding covert had obvious attractions and it was many years before the problems arose. *Mahonia*, originally planted as game cover, has colonised quite extensive areas of pine forest in East Anglia but apparently to no harmful effect.

The value of shrubs as a source of food is limited. Pheasants have very catholic tastes, and finding a pheasant's crop full of a particular type of berry does not mean that you have discovered the answer to a gamebird's dreams. If the bird had been shot the day before, its crop might well have been full of buttercup roots or even your own crocus bulbs!

Accessibility is also important, and small songbirds usually have first choice of the fruits of the taller shrubs, the pheasants mostly eating those that have fallen to the ground, often the remains of those dropped by the songbirds.

During the 1950s simple palatability tests were carried out at Fordingbridge by offering a variety of berries to penned pheasants under strictly controlled conditions, but the results were probably very suspect where they were negative. For instance, a type of *Berberis* berry was consistently refused but subsequently the crop of a pheasant, shot in the wild, was found to be crammed with them. The degree of ripeness of the berry, its accessibility and the availability of alternative foods obviously influence choice and this is difficult, if not impossible, to reproduce accurately in a trial. Sea buckthorn was the only berry taken in the trials when grain was offered as an alternative.

Many years ago, I organised the collection of sample crops from cock pheasants taken during every month of the year and from areas where no hand-feeding had taken place. Similar collections were made in Germany and Czechoslovakia and their contents analysed in Germany. The most significant information that came out of this concerned the crop contents of quite a small number of birds (about sixty) taken in England during January and February. Although this is probably the most difficult time of the year for a pheasant to find sufficient to eat, these crops contained no less than thirty-seven different types of food which shows how efficient the pheasant is at searching.

Berried shrubs are probably not of vital importance but they obviously provide some variety to a pheasant's diet and should always be included for this reason alone. It is, therefore, important to achieve the right balance when selecting shrubs. Species which produce berries do not usually provide the best ground cover and are sometimes armed with formidable thorns, while many good ground cover plants produce no berries at all, for example, *Lonicera nitida*. Give cover plants priority, therefore, since their value is known, but include a few berry-bearing species among them. Cost is also an important consideration and cover plants are usually much cheaper than those bearing berries. A simple example is a group of four *Lonicera nitida* with a single *Cotoneaster simonsii* in the middle. *Cotoneasters* are easy to establish in most sites and often more reliable than other species when producing berries.

To summarise, before making your choice, consider the following:

1. Note the principal features of the site: soil, aspect and climate.
2. Choose the tree species to be planted and note the density of canopy they will produce.
3. Go through the list of shrubs and note all those which will tolerate these conditions.
4. Find out from nurseries the availability of these shrubs and their cost.
5. With this in mind, design the pattern in which you are going to plant, perhaps including a few unusual types to add beauty and variety to your covert.

DEFENCES AGAINST INTRUDERS

Trouble comes from increasing pressure from the urban population, large-scale thefts of gamebirds from release pens and poaching. There are also those people who will dump anything in your wood from a mattress to a motor car. The gamekeeper, with much more land to police than his forebears, is hard pressed to deal with these problems even when provided with transport. It therefore makes sense to try to limit entry points to the coverts to as few places as possible and this is most important where they are bounded by a road, track or footpath. Barbed-wire fences are easily crossed but the kind known as Danert wire, which is coiled, opens up like a concertina and is much favoured by the army, does make a splendid hazard. Unfortunately, it is expensive although, since it is self-supporting and 50m (55yd) lengths can be erected in minutes, it is probably no more expensive than the usual post-and-wire fence.

A growing defensive hedge can be very effective and there are many suitable plant species to choose from, many of them very handsome as well. Of the native species, hawthorn, gorse, blackthorn and dog rose are all excellent for the purpose, particularly if planted as a mixture. Other suitable but more exotic species include barberry, firethorn, sweet briar and ramanas rose. It is not difficult to plan a very attractive defensive hedge for a car park, for instance, using these ornamental species backed up with the taller hawthorn and blackthorn behind them. Make sure, though, that there is sufficient light for a roadside hedge to grow well. This often means that some of the woodland edge must be cleared away before planting. If you want an absolutely impenetrable mixture, then have a back row of hawthorn, blackthorn and firethorn, a middle row of gorse and *Berberis*, then a row of Danert wire and in front of it ramanas rose, dog rose and sweet briar. Only a bulldozer could get through that!

SHRUBS FOR GAME COVERTS

Barberry *(Berberis)*
There are many sub-species and varieties of this shrub, the one most commonly planted being *thunbergii*. It has prolific berries but many sharp thorns. It is useful in a defensive hedge or as individual plants in a covert, but groups would be unpopular with beaters.

Box *(Buxus sempervirens)*
A favourite choice in game covert plantings in the early part of this century. Old plants can often indicate where the birds were flushed in

earlier times. It is excellent under heavy shade but very slow growing, although it can reach a height of 6–7m (20–23ft). It does well on all soils including chalk.

Bramble or blackberry *(Rubus fruticosus)*
It might be thought odd to include this species because in so many places we take it for granted and often it becomes a nuisance. Nevertheless, it is useful to include a few in a new game covert planted on farmland where it can be many years before the site is colonised naturally by shrubs. It is best planted when the trees have been in for three or four years to make sure that it does not hinder their growth. Groups of two or three plants with 20m (60ft) between the groups are all that is required. There are many varieties in the wild and some can be tremendously vigorous in growth and should obviously be avoided, but it is not difficult to select suitable types if they are growing naturally in nearby woodland and hedgerows, and suckers transplant easily.

Broom *(Cytisus)*
There are many garden varieties but the common broom, *Cytisus scoparius*, is the one mostly used for game. It is not tolerant of shade but is often planted as a flushing or holding area in open spaces. It is particularly suitable on dry, sandy soils and is useful for coastal sites. It is very short lived but in the right conditions will readily re-seed.

Buckthorn *(Rhamnus)*
The common hedgerow variety, *R. cathartica*, is a useful, spiny defensive plant which is recommended for shallow, chalk soils. *R. frangula*, the alder buckthorn, grows well in moist sites and has no spines. Both are deciduous and tolerant of chalk and shade. They provide good autumn colours.

Cherry family *(Prunus)*
A large group but only a few are of interest to game conservation and mainly these are laurels. *P. laurocerasus* (the cherry or common laurel) and *P. lusitanica* (the Portugal laurel) make really excellent tall shelter and can be coppiced if they become too high. In contrast to *Rhododendron ponticum*, they are reasonably easy for beaters to get through. They are wonderfully tolerant of shade and will prosper under the dense canopy of a beech wood. They must, however, be well established before the canopy closes. Another useful laurel is *P. zabelliana*, a narrow-leaved variety that does not grow much higher than 2m (6ft) but tends to spread outwards and provide good ground

cover. It can be rather slow growing, however. There is one more *Prunus* that has its uses but has nothing in common with laurel except its family name. *P. spinosa*, the blackthorn or sloe, can make a splendid defensive plant if included in a hedgerow of mixed species – its thorns can be very painful! All these plants are suitable in any soil, including chalk.

Cotoneaster

A large group of plants with sixty or more sub-species and varieties, most of them producing good berry crops of a suitable size for pheasants. They grow well on almost any soil and tolerate shade. Usually they are very quick to establish and they can be easily grown from seed. The following varieties are useful:

Larger varieties:	*Small to medium varieties:*
C. bullatus (floribundus)	C. horizontalis
C. cornubia	C. distichus
C. frigidus	C. simonsii
C. salicifolius	C. conspicuus
	C. franchetii
	C. microphyllus

My own favourite medium variety is *distichus*. In one trial planting, it was the only *Cotoneaster* which remained completely untouched by roe deer, though this cannot be guaranteed in every situation. My favourite large varieties are *frigidus* and *cornubia*, both of which can be coppiced if they get too tall. *Microphyllus* is a very low-growing variety whose fruits are readily accessible to pheasants.

Dogwood *(Cornus)*

There are many sub-species and varieties, but the most commonly used are *C. alba*, the red dogwood, and *C. stolonifera flaviramea*, which has greenish yellow stems. It is of medium height but it can spread into dense thickets. It is suitable for damp sites and useful as a low shelter screen around a flight pond. It tolerates shade quite well.

Elaeagnus

A useful plant for exposed coastal sites and one which makes an excellent shelter hedge. There are a number of sub-species and varieties to choose from but the most commonly used and a vigorous variety is *ebbingei*. *Elaegnus* is suitable for most soils but is not good under shade.

Escallonia

This has similar useful features to *Elaeagnus* with the addition of handsome flowers. There are many varieties to choose from and all are evergreen and tolerant of lime and drought. Most of them will stand up to salt winds, *E. macrantha* and *E. punctata* and 'Donard Radiance' particularly so.

Firethorn *(Pyracantha)*
Another good defensive plant. It is evergreen, extremely tough and well provided with thorns and useful berries. It will grow in any soil but does not prosper under shade.

Gaultheria
G. shallon is a lover of acid soil and this plant can sometimes be seen with heather in the New Forest area. It is not often planted for game, although frequently recommended in books on the subject. Pheasants and grouse are said to like its berries but I cannot vouch for this. It is a small to medium-sized evergreen plant which is tolerant of shade but hates chalk in the soil.

Gorse *(Ulex europaeus)*
A fine defensive plant and one of the most beautiful in the countryside when in full flower. It is a great pioneer plant, especially on poor and dry soils. Normally it is well behaved but when burnt or churned up by heavy machinery it can spread like mustard and cress; hence the great sweeps of it to be seen after the construction of new motorways. Like tamarisk, it can be a useful shelter plant in coastal sites and makes a virtually impenetrable hedge. It is very useful when planting on the site of old gravel workings. I would only use it as a perimeter hedge for a game covert: it is not advisable to plant it inside. It does not like chalk. I would advise using small pot-grown plants which must be kept free of weed until they are well established. Gorse does not transplant easily and I have had no success with seedlings dug up from a plantation.

Griselinia
G. littoralis is rather similar in appearance to *Elaeagnus* and is an evergreen plant, good for hedging in any soil and, as its name would suggest, useful in coastal sites. It is not too good under shade.

Hawthorn *(Crataegus monogyna)* (see also under tree section)
A valuable native species harbouring many useful insects (to the farmer as well as the game manager) and producing a good crop of berries. Its many sharp thorns can make it a useful defensive plant. Although usually regarded as a shrub, it can grow into a sizeable tree

10m (30ft) or more in height and a number of small tree sub-species and varieties are listed in the tree section. It is much favoured as a roost by pheasants, reasonably tolerant of shade, suitable for most soils and very hardy.

Hypericum

The variety *H. calycinum* (commonly called Rose of Sharon) is often planted in coverts but is not impressive. It is too low and dense for pheasants. On the other hand, the garden variety, 'Hidcote', makes an excellent, colourful cover plant since it is of medium height and semi-evergreen. It will grow well on most soils including chalk and is reasonably tolerant of shade.

Juniper *(Juniperus)*

Juniperus communis, the common juniper, is the native dwarf conifer of our chalk downlands but is not easily obtained. On the other hand, the garden sub-species *pfitzerana* and its varieties make excellent ground cover with their low, wide-spreading growth and are suitable for any soil. They are very useful in a flushing point and can be quite widely spaced, 3–4m (10–13ft) is about right.

Nine bark *(Physocarpus opulifolius [Luteus])*

This plant is often grown in West German deciduous forests where it is commonly called the 'pheasant spiraea'. I have planted a lot in Britain during the past ten years and find it a useful deciduous cover species. It can grow up to 3m (10ft) in full sunshine but will usually stop at 1–1.5m (3–5ft) under light shade. It is happy in all soils including chalk and should be planted in bold groups of ten to fifteen at 2m (6ft) spacing between the plants.

Oregon grape *(Mahonia aquifolium)*

This was often planted for game cover in the past. Indeed, in Thetford Forest it is now the dominant shrub cover in quite extensive areas and makes a welcome contrast to dense brambles. There are many other *Mahonias* available but *M. aquifolium* looks to be the only useful one for our purpose. Evergreen and of medium height, it is suitable for pretty well every soil, particularly chalk, and tolerates shade well. It is not known whether its berries are favoured by pheasants, certainly I have never heard it said so.

Pea tree *(Caragana arborescens)*

At present this shrub is not grown in any quantity in Great Britain, which is a pity because it could be very useful in areas with severe winter weather. In North America it is used extensively beside high-ways to collect drifting snow and seems quite happy in temperatures which drop far below anything normally experienced in the UK. It is not evergreen but becomes very dense when regularly trimmed and so should provide good shelter. It is a leguminous plant and produces seed in a pea-type pod but I am unable to say whether gamebirds would eat the seeds.

Pheasant berry *(Leycesteria formosa)*
It is not known why this is called the pheasant berry and there is no evidence that pheasants particularly favour the berries. Retailers do not like it since it usually gets frosted in the nursery. It is not worth planting for this reason, and I include it here only for curiosity.

Privet *(Ligustrum)*
This was much used as a cover plant and for hedges in earlier days. *L. ovalifolium*, the oval-leaved variety commonly used as a garden hedging plant, can provide good evergreen shelter but only if it is regularly managed. If left untended it quickly becomes 'leggy' and bare at the base. If this happens it can be partly cut through and laid flat when it will usually continue to grow and give good cover. In contrast, the wild privet, *L. vulgare*, can make a dense semi-evergreen hedge but it has an unfortunate habit of suckering and spreading into a thicket. Nevertheless, *L. vulgare* is useful in chalkland sites, particularly around the perimeter of bare-floored beech spinneys where partial shade suppresses some of its vigour.

Rose *(Rosa)*
No need to introduce the vast family of roses! There are three which are useful in covert planting. *R. canina*, the common dog rose, is always worth including. Pheasants like to eat the hips in winter and, provided that they are planted separately and not in groups, they are no trouble to beaters. They may also be included in a defensive hedge. *R. rubiginosa*, the sweet briar, also makes a handsome addition to any planting. Excellent defensive hedges can be made from *R. rugosa*, the ramanas rose, which is extensively used as a wildlife plant in Scandinavia.

Rosemary *(Rosmarinus officinalis)*
An excellent medium-sized evergreen shrub which can make very good light cover. Although it needs sunshine, it can be a useful plant in open spaces on chalkland. It is also, of course, a valuable herb in the kitchen and could be a useful cash crop if professionally managed.

Sea buckthorn *(Hippophae rhamnoides)*

In trials at Fordingbridge some years ago, sea buckthorn berries were the only ones which pheasants ate when wheat was available as an alternative. It can grow into dense thickets, particularly on sandy soils, and this can be seen in the belt of sand dunes which runs north along the coast from the Hague in Holland where, it is said, so many of the berries are eaten by pheasants that their flesh becomes bitter and unpalatable! However, a few should be planted in a covert, in groups to ensure pollination of females. It is suitable for all soils but does not like too much shade and has very long, sharp thorns.

Shrub honeysuckle *(Lonicera nitida)*

In many ways a very valuable plant, particularly for its evergreen shelter. It makes a wonderful hedge to warm up a covert. It is rarely eaten by rabbits, hares or deer and seldom needs any management, certainly not when grown as a perimeter hedge. It will grow on any soil and is easily struck from cuttings but does not prosper under shade. There are similar varieties to *L. nitida* such as *L. pileata* and *L. yunnanensis.*

Snowberry *(Symphoricarpos)*

This medium-sized deciduous species was extensively planted in game coverts in the early part of the century. Its habit of spreading vigorously by suckers has given it a bad name, but in the right site, under light shade, it can be very useful and does not misbehave. The berries do not appear to be palatable to pheasants but it is said that when the berries drop to the ground and start to rot both pheasants and partridges will eat the exposed seeds or 'pips'. The pink-berried variety, magic berry, is a smaller plant and not so vigorous. Snowberries can be planted in any soil, including chalk. I remember a gamekeeper saying that he liked them in a flushing point because they 'rattle well when tapped with the beaters' sticks'.

Spindle *(Euonymus)*

E. europaeus, the common spindleberry, which is such a handsome feature of our hedgerows, particularly in the chalklands, is deciduous. It is always a good idea to plant a few where the site is suitable, but the evergreen variety *E. japonicus* would also be useful as a shelter and cover plant. They will grow well in most soils and tolerate shade quite well.

Spiraea

This is a much neglected medium-sized cover plant which can be very effective in a game covert. The variety *S. salicifolia* (the bridewort), is widely distributed in Wales and will grow well under light shade but is not easily obtained from nurseries. *S. nipponica, S. thunbergii, S. x vanhouttei* and *S. veitchii* are also useful plants. Although the *Spiraeas* will grow in pretty well any soil they mostly have a habit of spreading by suckers, particularly *S. salicifolia*, and should not be planted too densely. Groups of three or four plants at 2m (6ft) spacing should be kept 10–15m (30–50ft) apart.

Spotted laurel *(Aucuba japonica)*
A medium-sized evergreen shrub which is suitable for all soils and situations and tolerates shade. It has male and female forms, the latter having small red berries.

Tamarisk *(Tamarix)*
Tamarix gallica is an excellent plant for exposed positions, particularly in coastal areas with salt-laden winds where it can be used very effectively to provide shelter for game coverts. It is not evergreen or dense growing and it does not like shade. It should therefore be planted in full sun on the windward side of the covert and at close spacing. To be really effective there should be three rows with the plants and rows at 1.5m (5ft) apart and the plants in staggered rows. *T. gallica* can be difficult to obtain but *T. pentandra* is very similar and usually readily available.

Viburnum
V. lantana, the wayfarer tree, and *V. opulus*, the guelder rose, are common plants widely distributed in Britain. Both have useful berry crops and wonderful autumn colours to the leaves. They prosper in any soil, including chalk, and the guelder rose is particularly good for marginally wet sites beside rivers, streams, lakes and marshes. They will tolerate light shade and can grow to 3 or 4m (10–13ft), but as they tend to get a bit leggy I regard them more as a food plant than as cover. They always make a very handsome addition to a covert.

Willow *(Salix)* (see also under tree section)
Among the enormous number of sub-species and varieties of the willow family there are some which can provide really good light, deciduous cover of medium height. In fact, all willows can be kept low by frequent coppicing (*S. viminalis*, the common osier, is the best example), but the following varieties will usually look after themselves: *S. purpurea*, the purple osier, *S. repens*, the creeping willow, and *S. lanata*, the woolly willow. It is commonly supposed that willows must have a wet site to

prosper but this is not so. They will grow almost anywhere except in exceptionally dry areas. Above all, they are extremely easy to propagate from cuttings, and these can often be taken from plants already on site and used with great effect to thicken up an existing game covert. They are a favourite food of roe deer and can be a useful buffer to divert their attention from more valuable species.

Appendix:
Scientific Names of Plants

alder, common	*Alnus glutinosa*
alder, grey	*Alnus incana*
alder, Italian	*Alnus cordoata*
amphibious bistort	*Polygonum amphibium*
apple, crab	*Malus spp.*
artichoke	*Helianthus tuberosa*
ash, common	*Fraxinus excelsior*
ash, mountain	*Sorbus aucuparia*
barberry	*Berberis spp.*
beech, common	*Fagus sylvatica*
beech, copper	*Fagus sylvatica purpurea*
birch, silver	*Betula pendula*
birch, white	*Betula pubescens*
bistort, amphibious	*Polygonum amphibium*
blackberry	*Rubus fruticosus*
blackthorn	*Prunus spinosa*
box	*Buxus*
bracken	*Pteris aquilinium*
bramble	*Rubus fruticosus*
briar, sweet	*Rosa rubiginosa*
broom	*Cytisus spp.*
buckthorn	*Rhamnus spp.*
bur-reed	*Sparganium erectum*
Canadian pondweed	*Elodea Canadensis*
canary grass	*Phalaris tuberosa*
cedar, western red	*Thuja plicata*
cherry, plum	*Prunus cerasifera*
cherry, wild	*Prunus avium*
chestnut, horse	*Aesculus hippocastanum*
chestnut, sweet	*Castanea sativa*
club rush, sea	*Scirpus maritima*
comfrey	*Symphytum officionale*
common alder	*Alnus glutinosa*
common ash	*Fraxinus excelsior*
common beech	*Fagus sylvatica*
common laurel	*Prunus laurocerasus*
common oak	*Quercus robur*
common privet	*Ligiustrum vulgare*
common whitebeam	*Sorbus aria*
copper beech	*Fagus sylvatica purpurea*
Corsican pine	*Pinus nigra maritima*

couch grass	*Agropyron repens*
cowslip	*Primula veris*
crab apple	*Malus spp.*
creeping willow	*Salix repens*
cricket bat willow	*Salix 'Caerulea'*
cypress, Lawson	*Chamaecyparis lawsoniana*
cypress, Leyland	*Cupressocyparis leylandii*
cypress, swamp	*Taxodium distichum*
dawn redwood	*Metasequoia glyptostroboides*
dog rose	*Rosa canina*
dogwood	*Cornus*
Douglas fir	*Pseudotsuga menziesii*
field maple	*Acer campestre*
fir, Douglas	*Pseudotsuga menziesii*
fir, giant	*Abies grandis*
firethorn	*Pyracantha spp.*
forget-me-not	*Myosotis spp.*
gean	*Prunus avium*
giant fir	*Abres grandis*
gorse	*Ulex europaeus*
grass, canary	*Phalaris tuberosa*
grass, couch	*Agropyron repens*
grey alder	*Alnus incana*
guelder rose	*Viburnum opulus*
hawthorn	*Crataegus spp.*
hazel	*Corylus avellana*
hemlock, western	*Tsuga heterophylla*
holly	*Ilex aquifolium*
honeysuckle, shrub	*Lonicera nitida*
horse chestnut	*Aesculus hippocastanum*
hypericum	*Hypericum calycinum*
Italian alder	*Alnus cordata*
juniper	*Juniperus spp.*
larch	*Larix spp.*
laurel, common	*Prunus laurocerasus*
Lawson cypress	*Chamaecyparis lawsoniana*
Leyland cypress	*Cupressocyparis leylandii*
lily, water	*Nymphoides spp.*
lime	*Tilia spp.*
lodgepole pine	*Pinus contorta*
London plane	*Platanus × hispanica*
maple	*Acer spp.*
marsh marigold	*Caltha palustris*
mint, water	*Mentha aquatica*
mountain ash	*Sorbus aucuparia*
mountain pine	*Pinus mugo*
nine bark	*Physocarpus opulifolius (Lutens)*
Norway spruce	*Picea abies*
oak, common	*Quercus robur*
oak, red	*Quercus rubra*
oleaster	*Elaeagnus angustifolia*

Oregon grape	*Mahonia aquifolium*
pea tree	*Caragana arborescens*
pear	*Pyrus*
pheasant berry	*Leycesteria formosa*
pine	*Pinus spp.*
pine, Corsican	*Pinus nigra maritima*
pine, lodgepole	*Pinus contorta*
pine, mountain	*Pinus mugo*
pine, Scots	*Pinus sylvestris*
plane, London	*Platanus × hispanica*
plantain, water	*Alisma plantago-aquatica*
plum, cherry	*Prunus cerasifera*
pondweed	*Potamogeten spp.*
pondweed, Canadian	*Elodea Canadensis*
poplar	*Populus spp.*
privet, common	*Ligustrum vulgare*
ramanas rose	*Rosa rugosa*
red oak	*Quercus rubra*
rose, dog	*Rosa canina*
rose, guelder	*Viburnum opulus*
Rose of Sharon	*Hypericum calycinum*
rose, ramanas	*Rosa rugosa*
rose, sweet briar	*Rosa rubiginosa*
rosemary	*Rosmarinus officinalis*
rowan	*Sorbus aucuparia*
Scots pine	*Pinus sylvestris*
sea buckthorn	*Hippophae rhamnoides*
sea club rush	*Scirpus maritima*
shrub honeysuckle	*Lonicera nitida*
silver birch	*Betula spp.*
Sitka spruce	*Picea sitchensis*
snowberry	*Symphoricarpos*
southern beech	*Nothofagus*
spindle	*Euonymus*
spruce	*Picea spp.*
spruce, Norway	*Picea abies*
spruce, Sitka	*Picea sitchensis*
standard thorn	*Crataegus spp.* (eg prunifolia, etc)
swamp cypress	*Taxodium distichum*
Swedish whitebeam	*Sorbus intermedia*
sweet briar	*Rosa rubiginosa*
sweet chestnut	*Castanea sativa*
sycamore	*Acer pseudoplatanus*
tamarisk	*Tamarix spp.*
thorn, standard	*Crataegus spp.* (eg prunifolia, etc)
walnut	*Juglans*
water lily	*Nymphoides spp.*
water mint	*Mentha aquatica*
water plantain	*Alisma plantago-aquatica*
wayfarer tree	*Viburnum lantana*
weeping willow	*Salix chrysocoma*

western hemlock	*Tsuga heterophylla*
western red cedar	*Thuja plicata*
whitebeam, common	*Sorbus aria*
whitebeam, Swedish	*Sorbus intermedia*
white willow	*Salix alba*
wild cherry	*Prunus avium*
willow, creeping	*Salix repens*
willow, cricket bat	*Salix*
willow, weeping	*Salix chrysocoma*
willow, white	*Salix alba*
willow, woolly	*Salix lanata*
woolly willow	*Salix lanata*
yellow iris	*Iris pseudacorus*
yew	*Taxus spp.*

The Game Conservancy

The Game Conservancy is an independent scientific and advisory organisation funded mainly by membership subscriptions, donations for specific projects and some research grants. Its parent body started operations over 50 years ago: in 1980 it became a registered charity.

Its main objective has always been to promote the conservation of game – including wildfowl and deer – in the British countryside. Advice is available to landowners, farmers, shoot managers and game-keepers, enabling them to improve the various habitats for game species. In the wake of good game management there invariably follows an increased survival of other wildlife: songbirds, butterflies and wild plants.

At present twelve scientists and six advisory consultants are employed. Investigating the pressures on farmland game is a priority – the effects of habitat destruction, the misuse of pesticides, changed cropping patterns and so on. Finding an acceptable compromise between food and timber production on the one hand and the survival of game in an attractive countryside is at the heart of their research. The pheasant and its woodland surroundings have been the subject of detailed studies, many of the practical issues being described in this work. Grouse have also been intensively researched: in particular, problems concerned with ticks and louping ill, strongylosis and population crashes and the significance of insects as a vital food source for chicks. Flooded gravel pits and their potential for wildfowl – and as fisheries – have been another area of Game Conservancy activities.

This is the organisation that inspired the author to write this book, and to which he was always grateful for a lifetime's interest and help.

Charles L. Coles
Former Director of The Game Conservancy

Index

Numbers in *italics* refer to illustrations

173

Service tree, 152
Sewelling, *53*, 54, *54*, 59–60, *59*, 76, 81, 93, 99, 100
Shade, 18, 23, 28–31 *passim*, 86, 112, 149, 160, 163, 166
Sheep, 93
Shelter, *16–17*, 18–30, *19–22*, 48, 67, 75, 78, 79, 82–93, *84–92, 110*, 114, 116, 129, 142, 147, 154–6; tree, 28, 78, 145
'Skylights', 58, 101, 110–11, *111*, 113–14, 123
Sleeves, 77–80 *passim*, 90, 109, 113, 116, 144, 145
Slugs, 125
Snowberry, *57*, 58–9, 61, 88, 157, 165
Softwoods, 44–6, 88, 153–6 *see also individual headings*
Sodium chlorate, 123
Spacing, 22, 23, *25*, 27, 29, 31, 34, 58, 59, 61, 66, 76, 77, 79, 80, 86, 87–8, 93, 117–20, 142, 144, 153
Spindle, 165
Spinneys, 13, *63*, 73–82, *75, 77, 78, 80–1*, 99, 114–16; instant, 76–82
Spiraea, 165–6
Spoilbanks, 134, 140–2
Spruce, 46, *56*; Norway, 24, 28, 35, 128, 155; Sitka, 28, 87, 104, *106*, 155
Staking, 145–7
Stetchworth Estate, *63*
Straw, *26*, 27, *29*, 39, 81, 124
Strimmers, 55
Studd, Sir Kynaston, 14, 77
Sunning, 33, 41
Sunlight, 14, 33, 46, 86, 88, 92
Sussex, 93
Sycamore, 36, 47, 150

Tamarisk, 166
Teal, 135
Thetford, 103–4, 107, 153, 163
Thinning, 10, 31, 34, 35, 40–1, 47, 88,

92, 101, *102*, 120, 122–3
Thistles, 36
Thorn, 36, 75, 86, 90, 114, 151
Thrips, 125
Thuja, 92
Topping, 28, 122
'Tramlining', 66
Transplants, 14, 76–8, 109, 144–5
Trout, 134, 140
Tubing, polythene, 146–7, *146*

Undergrowth, 31, 37, 41, 46, 47, 58
Underplanting, 14, 47
USA, 83, 131

Venturi effect, 82, *83*, 86
Viburnum, 166
Vole damage, 81

Wales, 166
Walls, 47, 93
Walnut, 152
Warmth, 46, 92, 153, 154
Warblers, 137
Water, 105–6, *106*, 131, 134–6 *see also* Pools/ponds
Waterfowl, 134, 135
Wayfarer tree, 24, 75, 166
Weeding, 31, 81, 87, 109, 120–2
Weeds, 27, 31, 76–9, 81, 121, 144, 145
West Suffolk, 12; *see also* Thetford
Wetland area, 131, *134–5*, 148
'Whips', 77–9, 109–11, *110, 111*, 114, 116, 145–6
Whitebeam, 29, 36, 74, 140, 147, 152; Swedish, 29, 74, 147, 152
Wildfowl, 135, 142, 172
Willow, 140, 142, 152–3, 166–7
Wind, 19, 28, 33, 39–40, 48, 67, 79, 82–93, 129, 130, 142, 154; baffles, 39–40, *70–1, 91*

Yew, 141, 156